THE UNIFORM EDITION OF
THE PLAYS OF J. M. BARRIE

THE OLD LADY SHOWS
HER MEDALS

THE PLAYS OF
J. M. BARRIE

THE OLD LADY SHOWS
HER MEDALS

HODDER AND STOUGHTON
PUBLISHERS   LONDON
1931

First printed . . . *September* 1918

Made and Printed in Great Britain for HODDER & STOUGHTON LTD.,
By T. and A. CONSTABLE LTD., Printers, Edinburgh.

FOUR PLAYS

THE OLD LADY SHOWS
HER MEDALS

THE OLD LADY SHOWS
HER MEDALS

THREE nice old ladies and a criminal, who is even nicer, are discussing the war over a cup of tea. The criminal, who is the hostess, calls it a dish of tea, which shows that she comes from Caledonia ; but that is not her crime.

They are all London charwomen, but three of them, including the hostess, are what are called professionally ' charwomen *and* ' or simply ' ands.' An ' and ' is also a caretaker when required ; her name is entered as such in ink in a registry book, financial transactions take place across a counter between her and the registrar, and altogether she is of a very different social status from one who, like Mrs. Haggerty, is a charwoman but nothing else. Mrs. Haggerty, though present, is not at the party by invitation ; having seen Mrs. Dowey buying the winkles, she followed her downstairs, and so has shuffled into the play and sat down in

3

it against our wish. We would remove her by force, or at least print her name in small letters, were it not that she takes offence very readily and says that nobody respects her. So, as you have slipped in, you can sit there, Mrs. Haggerty; but keep quiet.

There is nothing doing at present in the caretaking way for Mrs. Dowey, our hostess; but this does not damp her, caretaking being only to such as she an extra financially and a halo socially. If she had the honour of being served with an income-tax paper she would probably fill in one of the nasty little compartments with the words, ' Trade—charring; Profession (if any)—caretaking.' This home of hers (from which, to look after your house, she makes occasionally temporary departures in great style, escorting a barrow) is in one of those what-care-I streets that you discover only when you have lost your way; on discovering them, your duty is to report them to the authorities, who immediately add them to the map of London. That is why we are now reporting Friday Street. We shall call it, in the rough sketch drawn for to-morrow's press, 'Street in which the criminal resided'; and you will find Mrs. Dowey's home therein marked with a X.

Her abode really consists of one room, but she maintains that there are two; so, rather than argue, let us say that there are two. The other one has no window, and she could not swish her old skirts in it without knocking something over; its grandest display is of tin pans and crockery on top of a dresser which has a lid to it; you have but to whip off the utensils and raise the lid, and, behold, a bath with hot and cold. Mrs. Dowey is very proud of this possession, and when she shows it off, as she does perhaps too frequently, she first signs to you with closed fist (funny old thing that she is) to approach softly. She then tiptoes to the dresser and pops off the lid, as if to take the bath unawares. Then she sucks her lips, and is modest if you have the grace to do the exclamations.

In the real room is a bed, though that is putting the matter too briefly. The fair way to begin, if you love Mrs. Dowey, is to say to her that it is a pity she has no bed. If she is in

her best form she will chuckle, and agree that
the want of a bed tries her sore ; she will keep
you on the hooks, so to speak, as long as
she can; and then, with that mouse-like movement again, she will suddenly spring the bed
on you.   You thought it was a wardrobe, but
she brings it down from the wall; and lo, a bed.
There is nothing else in her abode (which we
now see to contain four rooms—kitchen, pantry,
bedroom, and bathroom) that is absolutely a
surprise; but it is full of ‘ bits,’ every one of
which has been paid ready money for, and
gloated over and tended until it has become
part of its owner.   Genuine Doweys, the dealers
might call them, though there is probably
nothing in the place except the bed that would
fetch half-a-crown.

Her home is in the basement, so that the
view is restricted to the lower half of persons
passing overhead beyond the area stairs.   Here
at the window Mrs. Dowey sometimes sits of a
summer evening gazing, not sentimentally at a
flower-pot which contains one poor bulb, nor
yearningly at some tiny speck of sky, but with

unholy relish at holes in stockings, and the like, which are revealed to her from her point of vantage. You, gentle reader, may flaunt by, thinking that your finery awes the street, but Mrs. Dowey can tell (and does) that your soles are in need of neat repair.

Also, lower parts being as expressive as the face to those whose view is thus limited, she could swear to scores of the passers-by in a court of law.

These four lively old codgers are having a good time at the tea-table, and wit is flowing free. As you can see by their everyday garments, and by their pails and mops (which are having a little tea-party by themselves in the corner), it is not a gathering by invitations stretching away into yesterday, it is a purely informal affair; so much more attractive, don't you think? than banquets elaborately pre-arranged. You know how they come about, especially in war-time. Very likely Mrs. Dowey met Mrs. Twymley and Mrs. Mickleham quite casually in the street, and meant to do no more than pass the time of day; then, naturally

enough, the word camouflage was mentioned,
and they got heated, but in the end Mrs.
Twymley apologised ; then, in the odd way in
which one thing leads to another, the winkle
man appeared, and Mrs. Dowie remembered
that she had that pot of jam and that Mrs.
Mickleham had stood treat last time ; and soon
they were all three descending the area stairs,
followed cringingly by the Haggerty Woman.

They have been extremely merry, and never
were four hard-worked old ladies who deserved
it better. All a woman can do in war-time
they do daily and cheerfully, just as their men-
folk are doing it at the Front; and now, with
the mops and pails laid aside, they sprawl
gracefully at ease. There is no intention on
their part to consider peace terms until a
decisive victory has been gained in the field
(Sarah Ann Dowey), until the Kaiser is put to
the right-about (Emma Mickleham), and sing-
ing very small (Amelia Twymley).

At this tea-party the lady who is to play the
part of Mrs. Dowey is sure to want to suggest
that our heroine has a secret sorrow, namely, the

crime; but you should see us knocking that idea out of her head! Mrs. Dowey knows she is a criminal, but, unlike the actress, she does not know that she is about to be found out; and she is, to put it bluntly in her own Scotch way, the merriest of the whole clanjamfry. She presses more tea on her guests, but they wave her away from them in the pretty manner of ladies who know that they have already had more than enough.

MRS. DOWEY. 'Just one more winkle, Mrs. Mickleham?' Indeed there is only one more.

But Mrs. Mickleham indicates politely that if she took this one it would have to swim for it. (The Haggerty Woman takes it long afterwards when she thinks, erroneously, that no one is looking.)

Mrs. Twymley is sulking. Evidently some one has contradicted her. Probably the Haggerty Woman.

MRS. TWYMLEY. 'I say it is so.'

THE HAGGERTY WOMAN. 'I say it may be so.'

MRS. TWYMLEY. 'I suppose I ought to know;

me that has a son a prisoner in Germany.'
She has so obviously scored that all good feeling seems to call upon her to end here. But she continues rather shabbily, 'Being the only lady present that has that proud misfortune.' The others are stung.

MRS. DOWEY. ' My son is fighting in France.'

MRS. MICKLEHAM. ' Mine is wounded in two places.'

THE HAGGERTY WOMAN. 'Mine is at Salonaiky.'

The absurd pronunciation of this uneducated person moves the others to mirth.

MRS. DOWEY. 'You'll excuse us, Mrs. Haggerty, but the correct pronounciation is Salonikky.'

THE HAGGERTY WOMAN, to cover her confusion. ' I don't think.' She feels that even this does not prove her case. ' And I speak as one that has War Savings Certificates.'

MRS. TWYMLEY. ' We all have them.'

The Haggerty Woman whimpers, and the other guests regard her with unfeeling disdain.

MRS. DOWEY, to restore cheerfulness, ' Oh, it's a terrible war.'

ALL, brightening, ' It is. You may say so,'

MRS. DOWEY, encouraged, ' What I say is, the men is splendid, but I'm none so easy about the staff. That's your weak point, Mrs. Mickleham.'

MRS. MICKLEHAM, on the defence, but determined to reveal nothing that might be of use to the enemy, ' You may take it from me, the staff's all right.'

MRS. DOWEY. 'And very relieved I am to hear you say it.'

It is here that the Haggerty Woman has the remaining winkle.

MRS. MICKLEHAM. ' You don't understand properly about trench warfare. If I had a map——'

MRS. DOWEY, wetting her finger to draw lines on the table. ' That's the river Sommy. Now, if we had barrages here——'

MRS. TWYMLEY. ' Very soon you would be enfilided. Where's your supports, my lady?' Mrs. Dowey is damped.

MRS. MICKLEHAM. ' What none of you grasps is that this is a artillery war——'

THE HAGGERTY WOMAN, strengthened by the

winkle, ' I say that the word is Salonaiky.'
The others purse their lips.

MRS. TWYMLEY, with terrible meaning, ' We 'll
change the subject.   Have you seen this week's
Fashion Chat ? '   She has evidently seen and
devoured it herself, and even licked up the
crumbs.   ' The gabardine with accordion
pleats has quite gone out.'

MRS. DOWEY, her old face sparkling.   ' My sakes !
You tell me ? '

MRS. TWYMLEY, with the touch of haughtiness
that comes of great topics, ' The plain smock
has come in again, with silk lacing, giving that
charming chic effect.'

MRS. DOWEY.   ' Oho ! '

MRS. MICKLEHAM.   ' I must say I was always
partial to the straight line '—thoughtfully re-
garding the want of line in Mrs. Twymley's
person—' though trying to them as is of too
friendly a figure.'

It is here that the Haggerty Woman's
fingers close unostentatiously upon a piece
of sugar.

MRS. TWYMLEY, sailing into the Empyrean, ' Lady

Dolly Kanister was seen conversing across the railings in a dainty *de jou.*'

MRS. DOWEY. ' Fine would I have liked to see her.'

MRS. TWYMLEY. ' She is equally popular as maid, wife, and munition-worker. Her two children is inset. Lady Pops Babington was married in a tight tulle.'

MRS. MICKLEHAM. ' What was her going-away dress ? '

MRS. TWYMLEY. ' A champagny cream velvet with dreamy corsage. She 's married to Colonel the Hon. Chingford—" Snubs," they called him at Eton.'

THE HAGGERTY WOMAN, having disposed of the sugar, ' Very likely he 'll be sent to Salonaiky.'

MRS. MICKLEHAM. ' Wherever he is sent, she 'll have the same tremors as the rest of us. She 'll be as keen to get the letters wrote with pencils as you or me.'

MRS. TWYMLEY. ' Them pencil letters ! '

MRS. DOWEY, in her sweet Scotch voice, timidly, afraid she may be going too far, ' And women in enemy lands gets those pencil letters and then stop getting them, the same as ourselves. Let's occasionally think of that.'

She has gone too far. Chairs are pushed back.

THE HAGGERTY WOMAN. ' I ask you ! '

MRS. MICKLEHAM. ' That's hardly language, Mrs. Dowey.'

MRS. DOWEY, scared, ' Kindly excuse. I swear to death I'm none of your pacifists.'

MRS. MICKLEHAM. ' Freely granted.'

MRS. TWYMLEY. ' I've heard of females that have no male relations, and so they have no man-party at the wars. I've heard of them, but I don't mix with them.'

MRS. MICKLEHAM. ' What can the likes of us have to say to them ? It's not their war.'

MRS. DOWEY, wistfully, ' They are to be pitied.'

MRS. MICKLEHAM. ' But the place for them, Mrs. Dowey, is within doors with the blinds down.'

MRS. DOWEY, hurriedly, ' That's the place for them.'

MRS. MICKLEHAM. ' I saw one of them to-day buying a flag. I thought it was very impudent of her.'

MRS. DOWEY, meekly, ' So it was.'

MRS. MICKLEHAM, trying to look modest with indifferent success, ' I had a letter from my son, Percy, yesterday.'

MRS. TWYMLEY. ' Alfred sent me his photo.'

THE HAGGERTY WOMAN. ' Letters from Salonaiky is less common.'

Three bosoms heave, but not, alas, Mrs. Dowey's. Nevertheless she doggedly knits her lips.

MRS. DOWEY, the criminal, ' Kenneth writes to me every week.' There are exclamations. The dauntless old thing holds aloft a packet of letters. ' Look at this. All his.'

The Haggerty Woman whimpers.

MRS. TWYMLEY. ' Alfred has little time for writing, being a bombardier.'

MRS. DOWEY, relentlessly, ' Do your letters begin " Dear mother " ? '

MRS. TWYMLEY. ' Generally.'

MRS. MICKLEHAM. ' Invariable.'

THE HAGGERTY WOMAN. ' Every time.'

MRS. DOWEY, delivering the knock-out blow. ' Kenneth's begin " Dearest mother." '

No one can think of the right reply.

MRS. TWYMLEY, doing her best, ' A short man, I should say, judging by yourself.'

She ought to have left it alone.

MRS. DOWEY. ' Six feet two—and a half.'

The gloom deepens.

MRS. MICKLEHAM, against her better judgment, ' A kilty, did you tell me ? '

MRS. DOWEY. ' Most certainly. He's in the famous Black Watch.'

THE HAGGERTY WOMAN, producing her handkerchief, ' The Surrey Rifles is the famousest.'

MRS. MICKLEHAM. ' There you and the King disagrees, Mrs. Haggerty. His choice is the Buffs, same as my Percy's.'

MRS. TWYMLEY, magnanimously, ' Give me the R.H.A. and you can keep all the rest.'

MRS. DOWEY. ' I'm sure I have nothing to say against the Surreys and the R.H.A. and the Buffs ; but they are just breeches regiments, I understand.'

THE HAGGERTY WOMAN. ' We can't all be kilties.'

MRS. DOWEY, crushingly. ' That's very true.'

MRS. TWYMLEY. It is foolish of her, but she

can't help saying it. 'Has your Kenneth great hairy legs ? '

MRS. DOWEY. 'Tremendous.'

The wicked woman : but let us also say 'Poor Sarah Ann Dowey.' For at this moment, enter Nemesis. In other words, the less important part of a clergyman appears upon the stair.

MRS. MICKLEHAM. 'It 's the reverent gent ! '

MRS. DOWEY, little knowing what he is bringing her, 'I see he has had his boots heeled.'

It may be said of Mr. Willings that his happy smile always walks in front of him. This smile makes music of his life, it means that once again he has been chosen, in his opinion, as the central figure in romance. No one can well have led a more drab existence, but he will never know it ; he will always think of himself, humbly though elatedly, as the chosen of the gods. Of him must it have been originally written that adventures are for the adventurous. He meets them at every street corner. For instance, he assists an old lady off a bus, and asks her if he

B

can be of any further help. She tells him
that she wants to know the way to Maddox
the butcher's.   Then comes the kind, triumphant smile; it always comes first, followed
by its explanation, ' I was there yesterday! '
This is the merest sample of the adventures that keep Mr. Willings up to the
mark.

Since the war broke out, his zest for life
has become almost terrible.   He can scarcely
lift a newspaper and read of a hero without
remembering that he knows some one of the
same name.   The Soldiers' Rest he is con-
nected with was once a china emporium, and
(mark my words), he had bought his tea
service at it.   Such is life when you are in
the thick of it.   Sometimes he feels that he
is part of a gigantic spy drama.   In the
course of his extraordinary comings and goings
he meets with Great Personages, of course,
and is the confidential recipient of secret
news.   Before imparting the news he does
not, as you might expect, first smile expan-
sively; on the contrary, there comes over his

face an awful solemnity, which, however, means the same thing. When divulging the names of the personages, he first looks around to make sure that no suspicious character is about, and then, lowering his voice, tells you, ' I had that from Mr. Farthing himself—he is the secretary of the Bethnal Green Branch,—h'sh ! '

There is a commotion about finding a worthy chair for the reverent, and there is also some furtive pulling down of sleeves, but he stands surveying the ladies through his triumphant smile. This amazing man knows that he is about to score again.

MR. WILLINGS, waving aside the chairs, ' I thank you. But not at all. Friends, I have news.'

MRS. MICKLEHAM. ' News ? '

THE HAGGERTY WOMAN. ' From the Front ? '

MRS. TWYMLEY. ' My Alfred, sir ? '

They are all grown suddenly anxious— all except the hostess, who knows that there can never be any news from the Front for her.

MR. WILLINGS. ' I tell you at once that all is
well. The news is for Mrs. Dowey.'

She stares.

MRS. DOWEY. ' News for me ? '

MR. WILLINGS. ' Your son, Mrs. Dowey—he has
got five days' leave.' She shakes her head
slightly, or perhaps it only trembles a little
on its stem. ' Now, now, good news doesn't
kill.'

MRS. TWYMLEY. ' We 're glad, Mrs. Dowey.'

MRS. DOWEY. ' You 're sure ? '

MR. WILLINGS. ' Quite sure. He has arrived.'

MRS. DOWEY. ' He is in London ? '

MR. WILLINGS. ' He is. I have spoken to him.'

MRS. MICKLEHAM. ' You lucky woman.'

They might see that she is not looking
lucky, but experience has told them how
differently these things take people.

MR. WILLINGS, marvelling more and more as he
unfolds his tale, ' Ladies, it is quite a romance.
I was in the —— ' he looks around cautiously,
but he knows that they are all to be trusted—
' in the Church Army quarters in Central
Street, trying to get on the track of one or

two of our missing men. Suddenly my eyes
—I can't account for it—but suddenly my
eyes alighted on a Highlander seated rather
drearily on a bench, with his kit at his feet.'

THE HAGGERTY WOMAN. ' A big man ? '

MR. WILLINGS. ' A great brawny fellow.' The
Haggerty Woman groans. ' " My friend," I
said at once, " welcome back to Blighty."
I make a point of calling it Blighty. " I
wonder," I said, " if there is anything I can
do for you ? " He shook his head. " What
regiment ? " I asked.' Here Mr. Willings
very properly lowers his voice to a whisper.
' " Black Watch, 5th Battalion," he said.
" Name ? " I asked. " Dowey," he said.'

MRS. MICKLEHAM. ' I declare. I do declare.'

MR. WILLINGS, showing how the thing was done,
with the help of a chair, ' I put my hand on
his shoulder as it might be thus. " Kenneth
Dowey," I said, " I know your mother." '

MRS. DOWEY, wetting her lips, ' What did he
say to that ? '

MR. WILLINGS. ' He was incredulous. Indeed, he
seemed to think I was balmy. But I offered

to bring him straight to you. I told him
how much you had talked to me about him.'

MRS. DOWEY. ' Bring him here ! '

MRS. MICKLEHAM. ' I wonder he needed to be
brought.'

MR. WILLINGS. ' He had just arrived, and was
bewildered by the great city. He listened to
me in the taciturn Scotch way, and then he
gave a curious laugh.'

MRS. TWYMLEY. ' Laugh ? '

MR. WILLINGS, whose wild life has brought him
into contact with the strangest people, ' The
Scotch, Mrs. Twymley, express their emotions
differently from us. With them tears signify
a rollicking mood, while merriment denotes
that they are plunged in gloom. When I had
finished he said at once, " Let us go and see
the old lady." '

MRS. DOWEY, backing, which is the first movement she has made since he began his tale,
' Is he—coming ? '

MR. WILLINGS, gloriously, ' He has come. He is
up there. I told him I thought I had better
break the joyful news to you.'

Three women rush to the window. Mrs. Dowey looks at her pantry door, but perhaps she remembers that it does not lock on the inside. She stands rigid, though her face has gone very grey.

MRS. DOWEY. ' Kindly get them to go away.'

MR. WILLINGS. ' Ladies, I think this happy occasion scarcely requires you.' He is not the man to ask of woman a sacrifice that he is not prepared to make himself. ' I also am going instantly.' They all survey Mrs. Dowey, and understand—or think they understand.

MRS. TWYMLEY, pail and mop in hand, ' I would thank none for their company if my Alfred was at the door.'

MRS. MICKLEHAM, similarly burdened, ' The same from me. Shall I send him down, Mrs. Dowey ? ' The old lady does not hear her. She is listening, terrified, for a step on the stairs. ' Look at the poor, joyous thing, sir. She has his letters in her hand.'

The three women go. Mr. Willings puts a kind hand on Mrs. Dowey's shoulder. He thinks he so thoroughly understands the situation.

MR. WILLINGS ' A good son, Mrs. Dowey, to have written to you so often.'

Our old criminal quakes, but she grips the letters more tightly. Private Dowey descends.

' Dowey, my friend, there she is, waiting for you, with your letters in her hand.'

DOWEY, grimly, ' That 's great.'

Mr. Willings ascends the stair without one backward glance, like the good gentleman he is ; and the Doweys are left together, with nearly the whole room between them. He is a great rough chunk of Scotland, howked out of her not so much neatly as liberally ; and in his Black Watch uniform, all caked with mud, his kit and nearly all his worldly possessions on his back, he is an apparition scarcely less fearsome (but so much less ragged) than those ancestors of his who trotted with Prince Charlie to Derby. He stands silent, scowling at the old lady, daring her to raise her head ; and she would like very much to do it, for she longs to have a first glimpse of her son. When he does speak, it is to jeer at her.

' Do you recognise your loving son, missis ? '

(' Oh, the fine Scotch tang of him,' she thinks.) ' I 'm pleased I wrote so often.' (' Oh, but he 's *raized*,' she thinks.) He strides toward her, and seizes the letters roughly. ' Let 's see them.'

There is a string round the package, and he unties it, and examines the letters at his leisure with much curiosity. The envelopes are in order, all addressed in pencil to Mrs. Dowey, with the proud words ' Opened by Censor ' on them. But the letter paper inside contains not a word of writing.

' Nothing but blank paper ! Is this your writing in pencil on the envelope ? ' She nods, and he gives the matter further consideration.

' The covey told me you were a charwoman ; so I suppose you picked the envelopes out of waste-paper baskets, or such like, and then changed the addresses ? ' She nods again ; still she dare not look up, but she is admiring his legs. When, however, he would cast the letters into the fire, she flames up with sudden spirit. She clutches them.

' Don't you burn them letters, mister.'

' They 're not real letters.'

' They 're all I have.'

He returns to irony. ' I thought you had a son ? '

' I never had a man nor a son nor anything. I just call myself Missis to give me a standing.'

' Well, it 's past my seeing through.'

He turns to look for some explanation from the walls. She gets a peep at him at last. Oh, what a grandly set-up man ! Oh, the stride of him. Oh, the noble rage of him. Oh, Samson had been like this before that woman took him in hand.

He whirls round on her. ' What made you do it ? '

' It was everybody's war, mister, except mine.' She beats her arms. ' I wanted it to be my war too.'

' You 'll need to be plainer. And yet I 'm d—d if I care to hear you, you lying old trickster.'

The words are merely what were to be

expected, and so are endurable; but he has moved towards the door.

'You 're not going already, mister ? '

'Yes, I just came to give you an ugly piece of my mind.'

She holds out her arms longingly. 'You haven't gave it to me yet.'

'You have a cheek ! '

She gives further proof of it. 'You wouldn't drink some tea ? '

'Me ! I tell you I came here for the one purpose of blazing away at you.'

It is such a roaring negative that it blows her into a chair. But she is up again in a moment, is this spirited old lady. 'You could drink the tea while you was blazing away. There 's winkles.'

'Is there ? ' He turns interestedly toward the table, but his proud Scots character checks him, which is just as well, for what she should have said was that there had been winkles. 'Not me. You 're just a common rogue.' He seats himself far from the table. 'Now, then, out with it. Sit down ! ' She sits meekly; there is nothing she would not do for him. 'As you char, I suppose you are on your feet all day.'

'I 'm more on my knees.'

'That 's where you should be to me.'

'Oh, mister, I 'm willing.'

'Stop it. Go on, you accomplished liar.'

'It 's true that my name is Dowey.'

'It 's enough to make me change mine.'

'I 've been charring and charring and charring as far back as I mind. I 've been in London this twenty years.'

'We 'll skip your early days. I have an appointment.'

'And then when I was old the war broke out.'

'How could it affect you ? '

'Oh, mister, that 's the thing. It didn't affect me. It affected everybody but me. The neighbours looked down on me. Even the posters, on the walls, of the woman saying, " Go, my boy," leered at me. I sometimes cried by myself in the dark. You won't have a cup of tea ? '

' No.'

' Sudden like the idea came to me to pretend I had a son.'

' You depraved old limmer ! But what in the name of Old Nick made you choose me out of the whole British Army ? '

Mrs. Dowey giggles. There is little doubt that in her youth she was an accomplished flirt. ' Maybe, mister, it was because I liked you best.'

' Now, now, woman.'

' I read one day in the papers, " In which he was assisted by Private K. Dowey, 5th Battalion, Black Watch." '

Private K. Dowey is flattered. ' Did you, now ! Well, I expect that 's the only time I was ever in the papers.'

Mrs. Dowey tries it on again. ' I didn't choose you for that alone. I read a history of the Black Watch first, to make sure it was the best regiment in the world.'

' Anybody could have told you that.' He is moving about now in better humour, and, meeting the loaf in his stride, he cuts a slice from it.   He is hardly aware of this, but Mrs. Dowey knows.   'I like the Scotch voice of you, woman.   It drummles on like a hill burn.'

' Prosen Water runs by where I was born.' Flirting again, ' May be it teached me to speak, mister.'

' Canny, woman, canny.'

' I read about the Black Watch's ghostly piper that plays proudly when the men of the Black Watch do well, and prouder when they fall.'

' There 's some foolish story of that kind.' He has another careless slice off the loaf. ' But you couldn't have been living here at that time or they would have guessed. I suppose you flitted ? '

' Yes, it cost me eleven and sixpence.'

' How did you guess the *K* in my name stood for Kenneth ? '

' Does it ? '

' Umpha.'

' An angel whispered it to me in my sleep.'

' Well, that 's the only angel in the whole black business.'   He chuckles.

'You little thought I would turn up!' Wheeling suddenly on her. 'Or did you?'

'I was beginning to weary for a sight of you, Kenneth.'

'What word was that?'

'Mister.'

He helps himself to butter, and she holds out the jam pot to him, but he haughtily rejects it. Do you think she gives in now? Not a bit of it.

He returns to sarcasm. 'I hope you're pleased with me now you see me.'

'I'm very pleased. Does your folk live in Scotland?'

'Glasgow.'

'Both living?'

'Ay.'

'Is your mother terrible proud of you?'

'Naturally.'

'You'll be going to them?'

'After I've had a skite in London first.'

The old lady sniffs. 'So she is in London!'

'Who?'

'Your young lady.'

' Are you jealyous ? '

' Not me.'

' You needna be.   She 's a young thing.'

' You surprises me.   A beauty, no doubt ? '

' You may be sure.'   He tries the jam.
' She 's a titled person.   She is equally popular as maid, wife and munition-worker.'

Mrs. Dowey remembers Lady Dolly
Kanister, so familiar to readers of fashionable gossip, and a very leery expression
indeed comes into her face.

' Tell me more about her, man.'

' She has sent me a lot of things, especially
cakes, and a worsted waistcoat, with a loving
message on the enclosed card.'

The old lady is now in a quiver of excitement.   She loses control of her arms, which
jump excitedly this way and that.

' You 'll try one of my cakes, mister ? '

' Not me.'

' They 're of my own making.'

' No, I thank you.'

But with a funny little run she is in the
pantry and back again.   She planks down a

cake before him, at sight of which he gapes.

'What's the matter? Tell me, oh, tell me, mister.'

'That's exactly the kind of cake that her ladyship sends me.'

Mrs. Dowey is now a very glorious old character indeed.

'Is the waistcoat right, mister? I hope the Black Watch colours pleased you.'

'Wha—at! Was it you?'

'I daredna give my own name, you see, and I was always reading hers in the papers.'

The badgered man looms over her, terrible for the last time.

'Woman, is there no getting rid of you!'

'Are you angry?'

He sits down with a groan.

'Oh, hell! Give me some tea.'

She rushes about preparing a meal for him, every bit of her wanting to cry out to every other bit, 'Oh, glory, glory, glory!' For a moment she hovers behind his chair. 'Kenneth!' she murmurs. 'What?' he asks, no longer aware that she is taking a liberty. 'Nothing,' she says, ' just Kenneth,' and is off gleefully for the tea-caddy. But when his tea is poured out, and he has drunk a saucerful, the instinct of self-preservation returns to him between two bites.

' Don't you be thinking, missis, for one minute that you have got me.'

' No, no.'

On that understanding he unbends.

' I have a theatre to-night, followed by a randy-dandy.'

' Oho ! Kenneth, this is a queer first meeting ! '

' It is, woman, oh, it is,' guardedly, ' and it 's also a last meeting.'

' Yes, yes.'

' So here 's to you—you old mop and pail. *Ave atque vale.*'

' What 's that ? '

' That means Hail and Farewell.'

' Are you a scholar ? '

' Being Scotch, there 's almost nothing I don't know.'

' What was you to trade ? '

' Carter, glazier, orraman, any rough jobs.'

' You 're a proper man to look at.'

' I 'm generally admired.'

' She 's an enviable woman.'

' Who ? '

' Your mother.'

' Eh ? Oh, that was just protecting myself from you. I have neither father nor mother nor wife nor grandmama.' Bitterly, ' This party never even knew who his proud parents were.'

' Is that '—gleaming—' is that true ? '

' It 's gospel.'

' Heaven be praised ! '

' Eh ? None of that ! I was a fool to tell you. But don't think you can take advantage of it. Pass the cake.'

' I daresay it 's true we 'll never meet again, Kenneth, but—but if we do, I wonder where it will be ? '

' Not in this world.'

' There 's no telling '—leering ingratiatingly—' It might be at Berlin.'

'Tod, if I ever get to Berlin, I believe I'll find you there waiting for me!'

'With a cup of tea for you in my hand.'

'Yes, and'—heartily—'very good tea too.'

He has partaken heavily, he is now in high good humour.

'Kenneth, we could come back by Paris!'

'All the ladies,' slapping his knees, 'likes to go to Paris.'

'Oh, Kenneth, Kenneth, if just once before I die I could be fitted for a Paris gown with dreamy corsage!'

'You're all alike, old covey. We have a song about it.' He sings:

> 'Mrs. Gill is very ill,
> Nothing can improve her
> But to see the Tuileries
> And waddle through the Louvre.'

No song ever had a greater success. Mrs. Dowey is doubled up with mirth. When she comes to, when they both come to, for there are a pair of them, she cries:

'You must learn me that,' and off she goes in song also:

> ' Mrs. Dowey's very ill,
>> Nothing can improve her.'

' Stop ! ' cries clever Kenneth, and finishes the verse :

> ' But dressed up in a Paris gown
>> To waddle through the Louvre.'

They fling back their heads, she points at him, he points at her.   She says ecstatically :

' Hairy legs ! '

A mad remark, which brings him to his senses; he remembers who and what she is.

' Mind your manners ! '   Rising, ' Well, thank you for my tea.   I must be stepping.'

Poor Mrs. Dowey, he is putting on his kit.

' Where are you living ? '

He sighs.

' That's the question.   But there's a place called The Hut, where some of the 2nd Battalion are.   They'll take me in.   Beggars,' bitterly, ' can't be choosers.'

' Beggars ? '

' I've never been here before.   If you knew'—a shadow coming over him—' what it

is to be in such a place without a friend. I
was crazy with glee, when I got my leave, at
the thought of seeing London at last, but after
wandering its streets for four hours, I would
almost have been glad to be back in the
trenches.'

' If you knew,' he has said, but indeed the
old lady knows.

' That 's my quandorum too, Kenneth.'

He nods sympathetically.

' I 'm sorry for you, you poor old body,'
shouldering his kit. ' But I see no way out
for either of us.'

A cooing voice says, ' Do you not ? '

' Are you at it again ! '

She knows that it must be now or never.
She has left her biggest guns for the end.
In her excitement she is rising up and down
on her toes.

' Kenneth, I 've heard that the thing a
man on leave longs for more than anything
else is a bed with sheets, and a bath.'

' You never heard anything truer.'

' Go into that pantry, Kenneth Dowey,

and lift the dresser-top, and tell me what you see.'

He goes. There is an awful stillness. He returns, impressed.

'It 's a kind of a bath!'

'You could do yourself there pretty, half at a time.'

'Me?'

'There 's a woman through the wall that would be very willing to give me a shake-down till your leave is up.'

He snorts.

'Oh, is there!'

She has not got him yet, but there is still one more gun.

'Kenneth, look!'

With these simple words she lets down the bed. She says no more; an effect like this would be spoilt by language. Fortunately he is not made of stone. He thrills.

'My word! That 's the dodge we need in the trenches.'

'That 's your bed, Kenneth.'

'Mine?' He grins at her. 'You queer old

divert. What can make you so keen to be burdened by a lump like me ? '

' He ! he ! he ! he ! '

' I tell you, I 'm the commonest kind of man.'

' I 'm just the commonest kind of old wifie myself.'

' I 've been a kick-about all my life, and I 'm no great shakes at the war.'

' Yes, you are. How many Germans have you killed ? '

' Just two for certain, and there was no glory in it. It was just because they wanted my shirt.'

' Your shirt ? '

' Well, they said it was their shirt.'

' Have you took prisoners ? '

' I once took half a dozen, but that was a poor affair too.'

' How could one man take half a dozen ? '

' Just in the usual way. I surrounded them.'

' Kenneth, you 're just my ideal.'

' You 're easily pleased.'

He turns again to the bed. 'Let's see how the thing works.' He kneads the mattress with his fist, and the result is so satisfactory that he puts down his kit.

'Old lady, if you really want me, I'll bide.'

'Oh! oh! oh! oh!'

Her joy is so demonstrative that he has to drop a word of warning.

'But, mind you, I don't accept you as a relation. For your personal glory, you can go on pretending to the neighbours; but the best I can say for you is that you're on your probation. I'm a cautious character, and we must see how you'll turn out.'

'Yes, Kenneth.'

'And now, I think, for that bath. My theatre begins at six-thirty. A cove I met on a 'bus is going with me.'

She is a little alarmed.

'You're sure you'll come back?'

'Yes, yes,' handsomely, 'I leave my kit in pledge.'

'You won't liquor up too freely, Kenneth?'

'You're the first,' chuckling, 'to care

whether I do or not.'   Nothing she has said
has pleased the lonely man so much as this.
'I promise. Tod, I'm beginning to look
forward to being wakened in the morning by
hearing you cry, "Get up, you lazy swine."
I've kind of envied men that had womenfolk
with the right to say that.'

He is passing to the bathroom when a
diverting notion strikes him.

'What is it, Kenneth?'

'The theatre. It would be showier if I
took a lady.'

Mrs. Dowey feels a thumping at her breast.

'Kenneth, tell me this instant what you
mean.   Don't keep me on the jumps.'

He turns her round.

'No, it couldn't be done.'

'Was it me you were thinking of?'

'Just for the moment,' regretfully, 'but
you have no style.'

She catches hold of him by the sleeve.

'Not in this, of course.   But, oh, Kenneth,
if you saw me in my merino! It's laced up
the back in the very latest.'

'Hum,' doubtfully; 'but let's see it.'

It is produced from a drawer, to which the old lady runs with almost indecent haste. The connoisseur examines it critically.

'Looks none so bad. Have you a bit of chiffon for the neck? It's not bombs nor Kaisers nor Tipperary that men in the trenches think of, it's chiffon.'

'I swear I have, Kenneth. And I have a bangle, and a muff, and gloves.'

'Ay, ay.' He considers. 'Do you think you could give your face less of a homely look?'

'I'm sure I could.'

'Then you can have a try. But, mind you, I promise nothing. All will depend on the effect.'

He goes into the pantry, and the old lady is left alone. Not alone, for she is ringed round by entrancing hopes and dreadful fears. They beam on her and jeer at her, they pull her this way and that; with difficulty she breaks through them and rushes to her pail, hot water, soap, and a looking-

glass. Our last glimpse of her for this evening shows her staring (not discontentedly)
at her soft old face, licking her palm,
and pressing it to her hair. Her eyes are
sparkling.

One evening a few days later Mrs. Twymley
and Mrs. Mickleham are in Mrs. Dowey's
house, awaiting that lady's return from some
fashionable dissipation. They have undoubtedly been discussing the war, for the
first words we catch are :

MRS. MICKLEHAM. ' I tell you flat, Amelia, I
bows no knee to junkerdom.'

MRS. TWYMLEY. ' Sitting here by the fire, you
and me, as one to another, what do you think
will happen after the war ? Are we to go
back to being as we were ? '

MRS. MICKLEHAM. 'Speaking for myself, Amelia,
not me. The war has wakened me up to a
understanding of my own importance that is
really astonishing.'

MRS. TWYMLEY. ' Same here. Instead of being
the poor worms the like of you and me thought

we was, we turns out to be visible departments of a great and haughty empire.'

They are well under weigh, and with a little luck we might now hear their views on various passing problems of the day, such as the neglect of science in our public schools. But in comes the Haggerty Woman, and spoils everything. She is attired, like them, in her best, but the effect of her is that her clothes have gone out for a walk, leaving her at home.

MRS. MICKLEHAM, with deep distaste, ' Here 's that submarine again.'

The Haggerty Woman cringes to them, but gets no encouragement.

THE HAGGERTY WOMAN. ' It 's a terrible war.'

MRS. TWYMLEY. ' Is that so ? '

THE HAGGERTY WOMAN. ' I wonder what will happen when it ends ? '

MRS. MICKLEHAM. ' I have no idea.'

The intruder produces her handkerchief, but does not use it. After all, she is in her best.

THE HAGGERTY WOMAN. ' Are they not back yet ? '

Perfect ladies must reply to a direct question.

MRS. MICKLEHAM. 'No,' icily. 'We have been waiting this half hour. They are at the theatre again.'

THE HAGGERTY WOMAN. 'You tell me! I just popped in with an insignificant present for him, as his leave is up.'

MRS. TWYMLEY. 'The same errand brought us.

THE HAGGERTY WOMAN. 'My present is cigarettes.'

They have no intention of telling her what their presents are, but the secret leaps from them.

MRS. MICKLEHAM. 'So is mine.'

MRS. TWYMLEY. 'Mine too.'

Triumph of the Haggerty Woman. But it is short-lived.

MRS. MICKLEHAM. 'Mine has gold tips.'

MRS. TWYMLEY. 'So has mine.'

The Haggerty Woman need not say a word. You have only to look at her to know that her cigarettes are not gold-tipped. She tries to brazen it out, which is so often a mistake.

THE HAGGERTY WOMAN. 'What care I? Mine is Exquisytos.'

No wonder they titter.

MRS. MICKLEHAM. 'Excuse us, Mrs. Haggerty (if that's your name), but the word is Exquiseetos.'

THE HAGGERTY WOMAN. 'Much obliged' (weeps).

MRS. MICKLEHAM. ' I think I heard a taxi.'

MRS. TWYMLEY. 'It will be her third this week.'

They peer through the blind. They are so excited that rank is forgotten.

THE HAGGERTY WOMAN. ' What is she in ? '

MRS. MICKLEHAM. ' A new astrakhan jacket he gave her, with Venus sleeves.'

THE HAGGERTY WOMAN. ' Has she sold her gabardine coat ? '

MRS. MICKLEHAM. 'Not her! She has them both at the theatre, warm night though it is. She 's wearing the astrakhan, and carrying the gabardine, flung careless-like over her arm.'

THE HAGGERTY WOMAN. ' I saw her strutting about with him yesterday, looking as if she thought the two of them made a procession.'

MRS. TWYMLEY. ' Hsh!' peeping. ' Strike me dead, if she 's not coming mincing down the stair, hooked on his arm ! '

Indeed it is thus that Mrs. Dowey enters.

Perhaps she had seen shadows lurking on the blind, and at once hooked on to Kenneth to impress the visitors. She is quite capable of it.

Now we see what Kenneth saw that afternoon five days ago when he emerged from the bathroom and found the old trembler awaiting his inspection. Here are the muff and the gloves and the chiffon, and such a kind old bonnet that it makes you laugh at once; I don't know how to describe it, but it is trimmed with a kiss, as bonnets should be when the wearer is old and frail. We must take the merino for granted until she steps out of the astrakhan. She is dressed up to the nines, there is no doubt about it. Yes, but is her face less homely? Above all, has she style? The answer is in a stout affirmative. Ask Kenneth. He knows. Many a time he has had to go behind a door to roar hilariously at the old lady. He has thought of her as a lark to tell his mates about by and by; but for some reason that he cannot fathom, he knows now that he will never do that.

MRS. DOWEY. 'Kenneth,' affecting surprise, 'we have visitors!'

DOWEY. 'Your servant, ladies.'

He is no longer mud-caked and dour. A very smart figure is this Private Dowey, and he winks engagingly at the visitors, like one who knows that for jolly company you cannot easily beat charwomen. The pleasantries that he and they have exchanged this week! The sauce he has given them. The wit of Mrs. Mickleham's retorts. The badinage of Mrs. Twymley. The neat giggles of the Haggerty Woman. There has been nothing like it since you took the countess in to dinner.

MRS. TWYMLEY. 'We should apologise. We're not meaning to stay.'

MRS. DOWEY. 'You are very welcome. Just wait'—the ostentation of this!—'till I get out of my astrakhan—and my muff—and my gloves—and' (it is the bonnet's turn now) 'my Excelsior.'

At last we see her in the merino (a triumph).

MRS. MICKLEHAM. 'You've given her a glory time, Mr. Dowey.'

D

DOWEY. 'It's her that has given it to me, missis.'

MRS. DOWEY. 'Hey! hey! hey! hey! He just pampers me,' waggling her fists. 'The Lord forgive us, but this being the last night, we had a sit-down supper at a restaurant!' Vehemently: 'I swear by God that we had champagny wine.' There is a dead stillness, and she knows very well what it means, she has even prepared for it: 'And to them as doubts my word—here's the cork.'

She places the cork, in its lovely gold drapery, upon the table.

MRS. MICKLEHAM. 'I'm sure!'

MRS. TWYMLEY. 'I would thank you, Mrs. Dowey, not to say a word against my Alfred.'

MRS. DOWEY. 'Me!'

DOWEY. 'Come, come, ladies,' in the masterful way that is so hard for women to resist; 'if you say another word, I'll kiss the lot of you.'

There is a moment of pleased confusion.

MRS. MICKLEHAM. 'Really, them sodgers!'

THE HAGGERTY WOMAN. 'The kilties is the worst!'

MRS. TWYMLEY. 'I'm sure,' heartily, 'we don't grudge you your treats, Mrs. Dowey; and sorry we are that this is the end.'

DOWEY. 'Yes, it's the end,' with a troubled look at his old lady; 'I must be off in ten minutes.'

The little soul is too gallant to break down in company. She hurries into the pantry and shuts the door.

MRS. MICKLEHAM. 'Poor thing! But we must run, for you'll be having some last words to say to her.'

DOWEY. 'I kept her out long on purpose so as to have less time to say them in.'

He more than half wishes that he could make a bolt to a public-house.

MRS. TWYMLEY. 'It's the best way.' In the important affairs of life there is not much that any one can teach a charwoman. 'Just a mere nothing, to wish you well, Mr. Dowey.'

All three present him with the cigarettes.

MRS. MICKLEHAM. 'A scraping, as one might say.'

THE HAGGERTY WOMAN. 'The heart,' enigmatically, 'is warm though it may not be gold-tipped.'

DOWEY. ' You bricks ! '

THE LADIES. ' Good luck, cocky.'

DOWEY. ' The same to you. And if you see a sodger man up there in a kilt, he is one that is going back with me. Tell him not to come down, but—but to give me till the last minute, and then to whistle.'

It is quite a grave man who is left alone, thinking what to do next. He tries a horse laugh, but that proves of no help. He says ' Hell ! ' to himself, but it is equally ineffective. Then he opens the pantry door and calls.

' Old lady.'

She comes timidly to the door, her hand up as if to ward off a blow.

' Is it time ? '

An encouraging voice answers her.

' No, no, not yet. I 've left word for Dixon to whistle when go I must.'

' All is ended.'

' Now, then, you promised to be gay. We were to help one another.'

' Yes, Kenneth.'

' It 's bad for me, but it 's worse for you.'

'The men have medals to win, you see.'

'The women have their medals too.' He knows she likes him to order her about, so he tries it again.

'Come here. No, I 'll come to you.' He stands gaping at her wonderingly. He has no power of words, nor does he quite know what he would like to say. 'God !'

'What is it, Kenneth ?'

'You 're a woman.'

'I had near forgot it.'

He wishes he was at the station with Dixon. Dixon is sure to have a bottle in his pocket. They will be roaring a song presently. But in the meantime—there is that son business. Blethers, the whole thing, of course— or mostly blethers. But it 's the way to please her.

'Have you noticed you have never called me son ? '

'Have I noticed it ! I was feared, Kenneth. You said I was on probation.'

'And so you were. Well, the probation 's ended.' He laughs uncomfortably.

' The like of me !   But if you want me you can have me.'

' Kenneth, will I do ? '

' Woman,' artfully gay, ' don't be so forward.   Wait till I have proposed.'

' Propose for a mother ? '

' What for no ? '   In the grand style, ' Mrs. Dowey, you queer carl, you spunky tiddy, have I your permission to ask you the most important question a neglected orphan can ask of an old lady ? '

She bubbles with mirth. Who could help it, the man has such a way with him.

' None of your sauce, Kenneth.'

' For a long time, Mrs. Dowey, you cannot have been unaware of my sonnish feelings for you.'

' Wait till I get my mop to you ! '

' And if you 're not willing to be my mother, I swear I 'll never ask another.'

The old divert pulls him down to her and strokes his hair.

' Was I a well-behaved infant, mother ? '

' Not you, sonny, you were a rampaging rogue.'

' Was I slow in learning to walk ? '

' The quickest in our street. He ! he ! he ! ' She starts up. ' Was that the whistle ? '

' No, no. See here. In taking me over you have, in a manner of speaking, joined the Black Watch.'

' I like to think that, Kenneth.'

' Then you must behave so that the ghost piper can be proud of you. 'Tion ! ' She stands bravely at attention. ' That 's the style. Now listen. I 've sent in your name as being my nearest of kin, and your allowance will be coming to you weekly in the usual way.'

' Hey ! hey ! hey ! Is it wicked, Kenneth ? '

' I 'll take the responsibility for it in both worlds. You see, I want you to be safeguarded in case anything hap——'

' Kenneth ! '

' 'Tion ! Have no fear. I 'll come back, covered with mud and medals. Mind you have that cup of tea waiting for me.' He is listening for the whistle. He pulls her on to his knee.

'Hey! hey! hey! hey!'

'What fun we'll have writing to one another! Real letters this time!'

'Yes.'

'It would be a good plan if you began the first letter as soon as I've gone.'

'I will.'

'I hope Lady Dolly will go on sending me cakes.'

'You may be sure.'

He ties his scarf round her neck.

'You must have been a bonny thing when you were young.'

'Away with you!'

'That scarf sets you fine.'

'Blue was always my colour.'

The whistle sounds.

'Old lady, you are what Blighty means to me now.'

She hides in the pantry again. She is out of sight to us, but she does something that makes Private Dowey take off his bonnet. Then he shoulders his equipment and departs. That is he laughing coarsely with Dixon.

We have one last glimpse of the old lady —a month or two after Kenneth's death in action. It would be rosemary to us to see her in her black dress, of which she is very proud; but let us rather peep at her in the familiar garments that make a third to her mop and pail. It is early morning, and she is having a look at her medals before setting off on the daily round. They are in a drawer, with the scarf covering them, and on the scarf a piece of lavender. First, the black frock, which she carries in her arms like a baby. Then her War Saving Certificates, Kenneth's bonnet, a thin packet of real letters, and the famous champagne cork. She kisses the letters, but she does not blub over them. She strokes the dress, and waggles her head over the certificates and presses the bonnet to her cheeks, and rubs the tinsel of the cork carefully with her apron. She is a tremulous old 'un; yet she exults, for she owns all these things, and also the penny flag on her breast. She puts them away in the drawer, the scarf over them, the lavender on the scarf. Her air of triumph well becomes her. She lifts the pail and the mop, and slouches off gamely to the day's toil.

THE NEW WORD

ANY room nowadays must be the scene, for any father and any son are the *dramatis personæ*. We could pick them up in Mayfair, in Tooting, on the Veldt, in rectories or in grocers' back parlours, dump them down on our toy stage and tell them to begin. It is a great gathering to choose from, but our needs are small. Let the company shake hands, and all go away but two.

The two who have remained (it is discovered on inquiry) are Mr. Torrance and his boy; so let us make use of them. Torrance did not linger in order to be chosen, he was anxious, like all of them, to be off; but we recognised him, and sternly signed to him to stay. Not that we knew him personally, but the fact is, we remembered him (we never forget a face) as the legal person who reads out the names of the jury before the court opens, and who

brushes aside your reasons for wanting to be
let off. It pleases our humour to tell Mr.
Torrance that we cannot let him off.

He does not look so formidable as when last
we saw him, and this is perhaps owing to our
no longer being hunched with others on those
unfeeling benches. It is not because he is
without a wig, for we saw him, on the occasion
to which we are so guardedly referring, both in
a wig and out of it ; he passed behind a screen
without it, and immediately (as quickly as we
write) popped out in it, giving it a finishing
touch rather like the butler's wriggle to his coat
as he goes to the door. There are the two
kinds of learned brothers, those who use the
screen, and those who (so far as the jury knows)
sleep in their wigs. The latter are the swells,
and include the judges; whom, however, we have
seen in the public thoroughfares without their
wigs, a horrible sight that has doubtless led
many an onlooker to crime.

Mr. Torrance, then, is no great luminary ;
indeed, when we accompany him to his house,
as we must, in order to set our scene properly,

we find that it is quite a suburban affair, only one servant kept, and her niece engaged twice a week to crawl about the floors. There is no fire in the drawing-room, so the family remain on after dinner in the dining-room, which rather gives them away. There is really no one in the room but Roger. That is the truth of it, though to the unseeing eye all the family are there except Roger. They consist of Mr., Mrs., and Miss Torrance. Mr. Torrance is enjoying his evening paper and a cigar, and every line of him is insisting stubbornly that nothing unusual is happening in the house. In the home circle (and now that we think of it, even in court) he has the reputation of being a somewhat sarcastic gentleman ; he must be dogged, too, otherwise he would have ceased long ago to be sarcastic to his wife, on whom wit falls like pellets on sandbags ; all the dents they make are dimples.

Mrs. Torrance is at present exquisitely employed ; she is listening to Roger's step overhead. You know what a delightful step the boy has. And what is more remarkable is that

Emma is listening to it too, Emma who is
seventeen, and who has been trying to keep
Roger in his place ever since he first compelled
her to bowl to him. Things have come to a
pass when a sister so openly admits that she is
only number two in the house.

Remarks well worthy of being recorded fall
from these two ladies as they gaze upward. ' I
think—didn't I, Emma ? ' is the mother's contribution, while it is Emma who replies in a
whisper, ' No, not yet ! '

Mr. Torrance calmly reads, or seems to read,
for it is not possible that there can be anything
in the paper as good as this. Indeed he occasionally casts a humorous glance at his womenfolk. Perhaps he is trying to steady them.
Let us hope he has some such good reason for
breaking in from time to time on their entrancing occupation.

' Listen to this, dear. It is very important.
The paper says, upon apparently good author-
ity, that love laughs at locksmiths.'

His wife answers without lowering her

eyes. ' Did you speak, John ? I am listening.'

' Yes, I was telling you that the Hidden Hand has at last been discovered in a tub in Russell Square.'

' I hear, John. How thoughtful.'

' And so they must have been made of margarine, my love.'

' I shouldn't wonder, John.'

' Hence the name Petrograd.'

' Oh, was that the reason ? '

' You will be pleased to hear, Ellen, that the honourable gentleman then resumed his seat.'

' That was nice of him.'

' As I,' good-naturedly, ' now resume mine, having made my usual impression.'

' Yes, John.'

Emma slips upstairs to peep through a keyhole, and it strikes her mother that John has been saying something. They are on too good terms to make an apology necessary. She observes blandly, ' John, I haven't heard a word you said.'

'I'm sure you haven't, woman.'

'I can't help being like this, John.'

'Go on being like yourself, dear.'

'Am I foolish?'

'Um.'

'Oh, but, John, how can you be so calm—with him up there?'

'He has been up there a good deal, you know, since we presented him to an astounded world nineteen years ago.'

'But he—he is not going to be up there much longer, John.' She sits on the arm of his chair, so openly to wheedle him that it is not worth his while to smile. Her voice is tremulous; she is a woman who can conceal nothing. 'You will be nice to him—to-night—won't you, John?'

Mr. Torrance is a little pained. 'Do I just begin to-night, Ellen?'

'Oh no, no; but I think he is rather—shy of you at times.'

'That,' he says a little wryly, 'is because he is my son, Ellen.'

'Yes—it's strange; but—yes.'

With a twinkle that is not all humorous, 'Did it ever strike you, Ellen, that I am a bit—shy of him?'

She is indeed surprised. 'Of Rogie!'

'I suppose it is because I am his father.'

She presumes that this is his sarcasm again, and lets it pass at that. It reminds her of what she wants to say.

'You are so sarcastic,' she has never quite got the meaning of this word, 'to Rogie at times. Boys don't like that, John.'

'Is that so, Ellen?'

'Of course I don't mind your being sarcastic to *me*——'

'Much good,' groaning, 'my being sarcastic to you! You are so seldom aware of it.'

'I am not asking you to be a mother to him, John.'

'Thank you, my dear.'

She does not know that he is sarcastic again. 'I quite understand that a man can't think all the time about his son as a mother does.'

E

' Can't he, Ellen ? What makes you so sure of that ? '

' I mean that a boy naturally goes to his mother with his troubles rather than to his father. Rogie tells me everything.'

Mr. Torrance is stung. ' I daresay he might tell me things he wouldn't tell you.'

She smiles at this. It is very probably sarcasm.

' I want you to be serious just now. Why not show more warmth to him, John ? '

With an unspoken sigh, ' It would terrify him, Ellen. Two men show warmth to each other ! Shame, woman ! '

' Two men ! ' indignantly. ' John, he is only nineteen.'

' That 's all,' patting her hand. ' Ellen, it is the great age to be to-day, nineteen.'

Emma darts in.

' Mother, he has unlocked the door ! He is taking a last look at himself in the mirror before coming down ! '

Having made the great announcement, she is off again.

' You won't be sarcastic, John ? '

' I give you my word—if you promise not to break down.'

Rashly, ' I promise.' She hurries to the door and back again. ' John, I 'll contrive to leave you and him alone together for a little.'

Mr. Torrance is as alarmed as if the judge had looked over the bench and asked where he was. ' For God's sake, woman, don't do that ! Father and son ! He 'll bolt ; or if he doesn't, I will.'

Emma Torrance flings open the door grandly, and we learn what all the to-do is about.

EMMA. ' Allow me to introduce 2nd Lieutenant Torrance of the Royal Sussex. Father—your son ; 2nd Lieutenant Torrance—your father. Mother—your little Rogie.'

Roger, in uniform, walks in, strung up for the occasion. Or the uniform comes forward with Roger inside it. He has been a very ordinary nice boy up to now, dull at his ' books ' ; by an effort Mr. Torrance had sent him to an obscure boarding-school, but at sixteen it was evident that an office was the proper place for Roger. Before the war broke out he was treasurer of the local lawn tennis club, and his golf handicap was seven; he carried his little bag daily to and from the city, and his highest relaxation was giggling with girls or about them. Socially he had fallen from the standards of the home; even now that he is in his uniform the hasty might say something clever about 'temporary gentlemen.' But there are great ideas buzzing in Roger's head, which would never have been there save for the war. At present he is chiefly conscious of his clothes. His mother embraces him with cries of rapture, while Mr. Torrance surveys him quizzically over the paper; and Emma, rushing to the piano, which is of such an old-fashioned kind that it can also be used as a sideboard, plays ' See the Conquering Hero Comes.'

ROGER, in an agony, ' Mater, do stop that chit making an ass of me.'

He must be excused for his ' mater.' That

was the sort of school; and his mother is rather proud of the phrase, though it sometimes makes his father wince.

MRS. TORRANCE. ' Emma, please, don't. But I 'm sure you deserve it, my darling. Doesn't he, John ? '

MR. TORRANCE, missing his chance, ' Hardly yet, you know. Can't be exactly a conquering hero the first night you put them on, can you, Roger ? '

ROGER, hotly, ' Did I say I was ? '

MRS. TORRANCE. ' Oh, John ! Do turn round, Rogie. I never did—I never did ! '

EMMA. ' Isn't he a pet ! '

ROGER. ' Shut up, Emma.'

MRS. TORRANCE, challenging the world, ' Though I say it who shouldn't—and yet, why shouldn't I ? '

MR. TORRANCE. ' In any case you will—so go ahead, " mater." '

MRS. TORRANCE. ' I knew he would look splendid; but I—of course I couldn't know that he would look quite so splendid as this.'

ROGER. ' I know I look a bally ass. That is why I was such a time in coming down.'

MR. TORRANCE. ' We thought we heard you upstairs strutting about.'

MRS. TORRANCE. ' John! Don't mind him, Rogie.'

ROGER, haughtily, ' I don't.'

MR. TORRANCE. ' Oh ! '

ROGER. ' But I wasn't strutting.'

MRS. TORRANCE. ' That dreadful sword ! No, I would prefer you not to draw it, dear—not till necessity makes you.'

MR. TORRANCE. ' Come, come, Ellen ; that 's rather hard lines on the boy. If he isn't to draw it here, where is he to draw it ? '

EMMA, with pride, ' At the Front, father.'

MR. TORRANCE. ' I thought they left them at home nowadays, Roger ? '

ROGER. ' Yes, mater ; you see, they are a bit in the way.'

MRS. TORRANCE, foolishly, ' Not when you have got used to them.'

MR. TORRANCE. ' That isn't what Roger means.'

(His son glares.)

EMMA, who, though she has not formerly thought much of Roger, is now proud to trot by his side and will henceforth count the salutes, 'I know what he means. If you carry a sword the snipers know you are an officer, and they try to pick you off.'

MRS. TORRANCE. 'It's no wonder they are called Huns. Fancy a British sniper doing that ! Roger, you will be very careful, won't you, in the trenches ? '

ROGER. 'Honour bright, mater.'

MRS. TORRANCE. 'Above all, don't look up.'

MR. TORRANCE. 'The trenches ought to be so deep that they can't look up.'

MRS. TORRANCE. 'What a good idea, John.'

ROGER. 'He's making game of you, mater.'

MRS. TORRANCE, unruffled, 'Is he, my own ?— very likely. Now about the question of provisions——'

ROGER. 'Oh, lummy, you talk as if I was going off to-night ! I mayn't go for months and months.'

MRS. TORRANCE. 'I know—and, of course, there is a chance that you may not be needed at all.'

ROGER, poor boy, 'None of that, mater.'

MRS. TORRANCE. 'There is something I want to ask you, John—How long do you think the war is likely to last?' Her John resumes his paper. 'Rogie, I know you will laugh at me, but there are some things that I could not help getting for you.'

ROGER. 'You know, you have knitted enough things already to fit up my whole platoon.'

MRS. TORRANCE, proud almost to tears, 'His platoon.'

EMMA. 'Have you noticed how fine all the words in -oon are? Platoon! Dragoon!'

MR. TORRANCE. 'Spitoon!'

EMMA. 'Colonel is good, but rather papaish; Major is nosey; Admiral of the Fleet is scrumptious, but Maréchal de France—that is the best of all.'

MRS. TORRANCE. 'I think there is nothing so nice as 2nd Lieutenant.' Gulping, 'Lot of little boys.'

ROGER. 'Mater!'

MRS. TORRANCE. 'I mean, just think of their cold feet.' She produces many parcels and displays their strange contents. 'Those are for putting inside your socks. Those are for outside your socks. I am told that it is also advisable to have straw in your boots.'

MR. TORRANCE. 'Have you got him some straw?'

MRS. TORRANCE. 'I thought, John, he could get it there. But if you think——'

ROGER. 'He's making fun of you again, mater.'

MRS. TORRANCE. 'I shouldn't wonder. Here are some overalls. One is leather and one fur, and this one is waterproof. The worst of it is that they are from different shops, and each says that the others keep the damp in, or draw the feet. They have such odd names, too. There are new names for everything nowadays. Vests are called cuirasses. Are you laughing at me, Rogie?'

MR. TORRANCE, sharply, 'If he is laughing, he ought to be ashamed of himself.'

ROGER, barking, 'Who was laughing?'

MRS. TORRANCE. 'John!'

Emma cuffs her father playfully.

MR. TORRANCE. 'All very well, Emma, but it's past your bedtime.'

EMMA, indignantly, 'You can't expect me to sleep on a night like this.'

MR. TORRANCE. 'You can try.'

MRS. TORRANCE. '2nd Lieutenant! 2nd Lieutenant!'

MR. TORRANCE, alarmed, 'Ellen, don't break down. You promised.'

MRS. TORRANCE. 'I am not going to break down; but—but there is a photograph of Rogie when he was very small——'

MR. TORRANCE. 'Go to bed!'

MRS. TORRANCE. 'I happen—to have it in my pocket——'

ROGER. 'Don't bring it out, mater.'

MRS. TORRANCE. 'If I break down, John, it won't be owing to the picture itself so much as because of what is written on the back.'

She produces it dolefully.

MR. TORRANCE. 'Then don't look at the back.'

He takes it from her.

MRS. TORRANCE, not very hopeful of herself, 'But I know what is written on the back,

" Roger John Torrance, aged two years four months, and thirty-three pounds." '

MR. TORRANCE. ' Correct.' She weeps softly. ' There, there, woman.' He signs imploringly to Emma.

EMMA, kissing him, ' I 'm going to by-by. 'Night, mammy. 'Night, Rog.' She is about to offer him her cheek, then salutes instead, and rushes off, with Roger in pursuit.

MRS. TORRANCE. ' I shall leave you together, John.'

MR. TORRANCE, half liking it, but nervous, ' Do you think it 's wise ? ' With a groan, ' You know what I am.'

MRS. TORRANCE. ' Do be nice to him, dear.' Roger's return finds her very artful indeed. ' I wonder where I put my glasses ? '

ROGER. ' I 'll look for them.'

MRS. TORRANCE. ' No, I remember now. They are upstairs in such a funny place that I must go myself. Do you remember, Rogie, that I hoped they would reject you on account of your eyes ? '

ROGER. ' I suppose you couldn't help it.'

MRS. TORRANCE, beaming on her husband, ' Did you believe I really meant it, John ? '

MR. TORRANCE, curious, ' Did *you*, Roger ? '

ROGER. ' Of course. Didn't you, father ? '

MR. TORRANCE. ' No ! I knew the old lady better.'

He takes her hand.

MRS. TORRANCE, sweetly, ' I shouldn't have liked it, Rogie dear. I 'll tell you something. You know your brother Harry died when he was seven. To you, I suppose, it is as if he had never been. You were barely five.'

ROGER. ' I don't remember him, mater.'

MRS. TORRANCE. ' No—no. But I do, Rogie. He would be twenty-one now ; but though you and Emma grew up I have always gone on seeing him as just seven. Always till the war broke out. And now I see him a man of twenty-one, dressed in khaki, fighting for his country, same as you. I wouldn't have had one of you stay at home, though I had had a dozen. That is, if it is the noble war they all say it is. I 'm not clever, Rogie, I have to take it on trust. Surely they wouldn't deceive mothers. I 'll get my glasses.'

She goes away, leaving the father and son somewhat moved. It is Mr. Torrance who speaks first, gruffly.

' Like to change your mother, Roger ? '

The answer is also gruff. ' What do *you* think ? '

Then silence falls. These two are very conscious of being together, without so much as the tick of a clock to help them. The father clings to his cigar, sticks his knife into it, studies the leaf, tries crossing his legs another way. The son examines the pictures on the walls as if he had never seen them before, and is all the time edging toward the door.

Mr. Torrance wets his lips ; it must be now or never, ' Not going, Roger ? '

Roger counts the chairs. ' Yes, I thought——'

' Won't you—sit down and—have a chat ? '

Roger is bowled over. ' A what ? You and me ! '

' Why not ? ' rather truculently.

' Oh—oh, all right,' sitting uncomfortably.

The cigar gets several more stabs.

' I suppose you catch an early train to-morrow ? '

' The 5.20. I have flag-signalling at half-past six.'

' Phew ! Hours before I shall be up.'

' I suppose so.'

' Well, you needn't dwell on it, Roger.'

Indignantly, ' I didn't.' He starts up. ' Good-night, father.'

' Good-night. Damn. Come back. My fault. Didn't I say I wanted to have a chat with you ? '

' I thought we had had it.'

Gloomily, ' No such luck.'

There is another pause. A frightened ember in the fire makes an appeal to some one to say something. Mr. Torrance rises. It is now he who is casting eyes at the door. He sits again, ashamed of himself.

' I like your uniform, Roger,' he says pleasantly.

Roger wriggles. 'Haven't you made fun of me enough?'

Sharply, 'I'm not making fun of you. Don't you see I'm trying to tell you that I'm proud of you?'

Roger is at last aware of it, with a sinking. He appeals, 'Good lord, father, *you* are not going to begin now.'

The father restrains himself.

'Do you remember, Roger, my saying that I didn't want you to smoke till you were twenty?'

'Oh, it's that, is it? Shutting his mouth tight, 'I never promised.'

Almost with a shout, 'It's not that.' Then kindly, 'Have a cigar, my boy?'

'Me?'

A rather shaky hand passes him a cigar case. Roger selects from it and lights up nervously. He is now prepared for the worst.

'Have you ever wondered, Roger, what sort of a fellow I am?'

Guardedly, 'Often.'

Mr. Torrance casts all sense of decency to

the winds; such is one of the effects of
war.

'I have often wondered what sort of fellow
you are, Roger. We have both been at it
on the sly. I suppose that is what makes
a father and son so uncomfortable in each
other's presence.'

Roger is not yet prepared to meet him half-
way, but he casts a line.

'Do you feel the creeps when you are left
alone with me?'

'Mortally, Roger. My first instinct is to
slip away.'

'So is mine,' with deep feeling.

'You don't say so!' with such surprise
that the father undoubtedly goes up a step
in the son's estimation. 'I always seem to
know what you are thinking, Roger.'

'Do you? Same here.'

'As a consequence it is better, it is right,
it is only decent that you and I should be
very chary of confidences with each other.'

Roger is relieved. 'I'm dashed glad you
see it in that way.'

' Oh, quite. And yet, Roger, if you had
to answer this question on oath, " Whom do
you think you are most like in this world ? "
I don't mean superficially, but deep down
in your vitals, what would you say ? Your
mother, your uncle, one of your friends on
the golf links ? '

' No.'

' Who ? '

Darkly, ' You.'

' Just how I feel.'

There is such true sympathy in the manly
avowal that Roger cannot but be brought
closer to his father.

' It 's pretty ghastly, father.'

' It is. I don't know which it is worse for.'

They consider each other without bitterness.

' You are a bit of a wag at times, Roger.'

' You soon shut me up.'

' I have heard that you sparkle more
freely in my absence.'

' They say the same about you.'

' And now that you mention it, I believe it
is true; and yet, isn't it a bigger satisfaction

F

to you to catch me relishing your jokes than
any other person ? '

Roger's eyes open wide. ' How did you
know that ? '

' Because I am so bucked if I see you
relishing mine.'

' *Are* you ? ' Roger's hold on the certain
things in life are slipping. ' You don't show
it.'

' That is because of our awkward relation-
ship.'

Roger lapses into gloom. ' We have got
to go through with it.'

His father kicks the coals. ' There 's no
way out.'

' No.'

' We have, as it were, signed a compact,
Roger, never to let on that we care for each
other.   As gentlemen we must stick to it.'

' Yes.   What are you getting at, father ? '

' There is a war on, Roger.'

' That needn't make any difference.'

' Yes, it does.   Roger, be ready ; I hate
to hit you without warning.   I 'm going to

cast a grenade into the middle of you. It 's
this, I 'm fond of you, my boy.'

Roger squirms. ' Father, if any one were
to hear you ! '

' They won't. The door is shut, Amy is
gone to bed, and all is quiet in our street.
Won't you—won't you say something civil
to me in return, Roger ? '

Roger looks at him and away from him.
' I sometimes—bragged about you at school.'

Mr. Torrance is absurdly pleased. ' Did
you ? What sort of things, Roger ? '

' I—I forget.'

' Come on, Roger.'

' Is this fair, father ? '

' No, I suppose it isn't.' Mr. Torrance
attacks the coals again. ' You and your
mother have lots of confidences, haven't
you ? '

' I tell her a good deal. Somehow——'

' Yes, somehow one can.' With the art-
fulness that comes of years, ' I 'm glad you
tell her everything.'

Roger looks down his cigar. ' Not everything, father. There are things—about one-self——'

' Aren't there, Roger ! '

' Best not to tell her.'

' Yes—yes. If there are any of them you would care to tell me instead—just if you want to, mind—just if you are in a hole or anything ? '

' No thanks,' very stiffly.

' Any little debts, for instance ? '

' That 's all right now. Mother——'

' She did ? '

Roger is ready to jump at him. ' I was willing to speak to you about them, but——'

' She said, " Not worth while bothering father." '

' How did you know ? '

' Oh, I have met your mother before, you see. Nothing else ? '

' No.'

' Haven't been an ass about a girl or any-thing of that sort ? '

' Good lord, father ! '

' I shouldn't have said it. In my young

days we sometimes——It 's all different now.'

' I don't know. I could tell you things that would surprise you.'

' No! Not about yourself ? '

' No. At least——'

' Just as you like, Roger.'

.' It blew over long ago.'

' Then there 's no need ? '

' No—oh no. It was just—you know—the old, old story.'

He eyes his father suspiciously, but not a muscle in Mr. Torrance's countenance is out of place.

' I see. It hasn't—left you bitter about the sex, Roger, I hope ? '

' Not now. She—you know what women are.'

' Yes, yes.'

' You needn't mention it to mother.'

' I won't.' Mr. Torrance is elated to share a secret with Roger about which mother is not to know. ' Think your mother and I are an aged pair, Roger ? '

' I never——of course you are not young.'

' How long have you known that ? I mean, it's true—but I didn't know it till quite lately.'

' That you're old ? '

' Hang it, Roger, not so bad as that— elderly. This will stagger you; but I assure you that until the other day I jogged along thinking of myself as on the whole still one of the juveniles.' He makes a wry face. ' I crossed the bridge, Roger, without knowing it.'

' What made you know ? '

' What makes us know all the new things, Roger ?—the war. I'll tell you a secret. When we realised in August of 1914 that myriads of us were to be needed, my first thought wasn't that I had a son, but that I must get fit myself.'

' You ! '

' Funny, isn't it ? ' says Mr. Torrance quite nastily. ' But, as I tell you, I didn't know I had ceased to be young. I went into Regent's Park and tried to run a mile.'

' Lummy, you might have killed yourself.'

' I nearly did—especially as I had put a weight on my shoulders to represent my kit. I kept at it for a week, but I knew the game was up. The discovery was pretty grim, Roger.'

' Don't you bother about that part of it. You are doing your share, taking care of mother and Emma.'

Mr. Torrance emits a laugh of self-contempt. ' I am not taking care of them. It is you who are taking care of them. My friend, you are the head of the house now.'

' Father ! '

' Yes, we have come back to hard facts, and the defender of the house is the head of it.'

' Me ? Fudge.'

' It 's true. The thing that makes me wince most is that some of my contemporaries have managed to squeeze back : back into youth, Roger, though I guess they were a pretty tight fit in the turnstile. There is Coxon; he is in khaki now, with his hair dyed, and when he and I meet at the club

we know that we belong to different genera-
tions. I'm a decent old fellow, but I don't
really count any more, while Coxon, lucky
dog, is being damned daily on parade.'

'I hate your feeling it in that way, father.'

'I don't say it is a palatable draught, but
when the war is over we shall all shake down
to the new conditions. No fear of my being
sarcastic to you then, Roger. I'll have to
be jolly respectful.'

'Shut up, father!'

'You've begun, you see. Don't worry,
Roger. Any rawness I might feel in having
missed the chance of seeing whether I was a
man—like Coxon, confound him!—is swal-
lowed up in the pride of giving the chance to
you. I'm in a shiver about you, but——
It's all true, Roger, what your mother said
about 2nd Lieutenants. Till the other day
we were so little of a military nation that
most of us didn't know there *were* 2nd Lieutenants. And now, in thousands of homes
we feel that there is nothing else. 2nd
Lieutenant! It is like a new word to us—

one, I daresay, of many that the war will add to our language. We have taken to it, Roger. If a son of mine were to tarnish it——'

'I 'll try not to,' Roger growls.

'If you did, I should just know that there had been something wrong about me.'

Gruffly, 'You 're all right.'

'If I am, you are.' It is a winning face that Mr. Torrance turns on his son. 'I suppose you have been asking yourself of late, what if you were to turn out to be a funk!'

'Father, how did you know?'

'I know because you are me. Because ever since there was talk of this commission I have been thinking and thinking what were you thinking—so as to help you.'

This itself is a help. Roger's hand—but he withdraws it hurriedly.

'They all seem to be so frightfully brave, father,' he says wistfully.

'I expect, Roger, that the best of them had the same qualms as you before their first engagement.'

'I—I kind of think, father, that I won't be a funk.'

'I kind of think so too, Roger.' Mr. Torrance forgets himself. 'Mind you don't be rash, my boy; and for God's sake, keep your head down in the trenches.'

Roger has caught him out. He points a gay finger at his anxious father.

'You know you laughed at mother for saying that!'

'Did I? Roger, your mother thinks that I have an unfortunate manner with you.'

The magnanimous Roger says, 'Oh, I don't know. It's just the father-and-son complication.'

'That is really all it is. But she thinks I should show my affection for you more openly.'

Roger wriggles again. Earnestly, 'I wouldn't do that.' Nicely, 'Of course for this once—but in a general way I wouldn't do that. *We* know, you and I.'

'As long as we know, it's no one else's affair, is it?'

'That's the ticket, father.'

' Still——' It is to be feared that Mr. Torrance is now taking advantage of his superior slyness. ' Still, before your mother —to please her—eh ? '

Faltering, ' I suppose it would.'

' Well, what do you say ? '

' I know she would like it.'

' Of course you and I know that display of that sort is all bunkum—repellent even to our natures.'

' Lord, yes ! '

' But to gratify her.'

' I should be so conscious.'

Mr. Torrance is here quite as sincere as his son. ' So should I.'

Roger considers it. ' How far would you go ? '

' Oh, not far. Suppose I called you " Old Rogie " ? There 's not much in that.'

' It all depends on the way one says these things.'

' I should be quite casual.'

' Hum. What would you like me to call you ? '

Severely, ' It isn't what would *I* like. But I daresay your mother would beam if you called me " dear father." '

' I don't think so.'

' You know quite well that you think so, Roger.'

' It 's so effeminate.'

' Not if you say it casually.'

With something very like a snort Roger asks, ' How does one say a thing like that casually ? '

' Well, for instance, you could whistle while you said it—or anything of that sort.'

' Hum. Of course you—if we were to— be like that, you wouldn't *do* anything.'

' How do you mean ? '

' You wouldn't paw me ? '

' Roger,' with some natural indignation, ' you forget yourself.' But apparently it is for him to continue. ' That reminds me of a story I heard the other day of a French general. He had asked for volunteers from his airmen for some specially dangerous job— and they all stepped forward. Pretty good that. Then three were chosen and got their orders and saluted, and were starting off when he stopped them. " Since when," he said, " have brave boys departing to the post of danger omitted to embrace their father ? " They did it then. Good story ? '

Roger lowers. ' They were French.'

' Yes, I said so. Don't you think it's good ? '

' Why do you tell it to me ? '

' Because it's a good story.'

' You are sure, father,' sternly, ' that there is no other reason ? ' Mr. Torrance tries to brazen it out, but he looks guilty. ' You know, father, that is barred.'

Just because he knows that he has been playing it low, Mr. Torrance snaps angrily, ' What is barred ? '

' You know,' says his monitor.

Mr. Torrance shouts.

' I know that you are a young ass.'

' Really, father——'

' Hold your tongue.'

Roger can shout also.

' I must say, father——'

' Be quiet, I tell you.'

It is in the middle of this competition that the lady who dotes on them both chooses to come back, still without her spectacles.

' Oh dear ! And I had hoped——Oh, John ! '

Mr. Torrance would like to kick himself. ' My fault,' he says with a groan.

' But whatever is the matter ? '

' Nothing, mater.' The war is already making Roger quite smart. ' Only father wouldn't do as I told him.'

Mr. Torrance cannot keep pace with his son's growth. He raps out, ' Why the dickens should I ? '

Roger is imperturbable ; this will be useful in France. ' You see, mater, he said I was the head of the house.'

' You, Rogie ! ' She goes to her husband's side. ' What nonsense ! '

Roger grins. ' Do you like my joke, father ? '

The father smiles upon him and is at once uproariously happy. He digs his boy boldly in the ribs.

' Roger, you scoundrel ! '

' That's better,' says Mrs. Torrance at a venture.

Roger feels that things have perhaps gone far enough. ' I think I 'll go to my room now. You will come up, mater ? '

' Yes, dear. I shan't be five minutes, John.'

' More like half an hour.'

She hesitates. ' There is nothing wrong, is there ? I thought I noticed a—a——'

' A certain liveliness, my dear. No, we were only having a good talk.'

' What about, John ? ' wistfully.

' About the war,' Roger breaks in hurriedly.

' About tactics and strategy, wasn't it, Roger ? '

' Yes.'

' The fact is, Ellen, I have been helping Roger to take his first trench.' With a big breath, ' And we took it too, together, didn't we, Roger ? '

' You bet,' says Roger valiantly.

' Though I suppose,' sighing, ' it is one of

those trenches that the enemy retake during the night.'

' Oh, I—I don't know, father.'

The lady asks, ' Whatever are you two talking about ? '

' Aha,' says Mr. Torrance in high feather, patting her, but unable to resist a slight boast, ' it is very private. *We* don't tell you everything, you know, Ellen.'

She beams, though she does not understand.

' Come on, mater, it 's only his beastly sarcasm again. 'Night, father; I won't see you in the morning.'

' 'Night,' says Mr. Torrance.

But Roger has not gone yet. He seems to be looking for something—a book, perhaps. Then he begins to whistle—casually.

' Good-night, dear father.'

Mr. John Torrance is left alone, rubbing his hands.

BARBARA'S WEDDING

THE Colonel is in the sitting-room of his country cottage, staring through the open windows at his pretty garden. He is a very old man, and is sometimes bewildered nowadays. He calls to Dering, the gardener, who is on a ladder, pruning. Dering, who comes to him, is a rough, capable young fellow with fingers that are already becoming stumpy because he so often uses his hands instead of a spade. This is a sign that Dering will never get on in the world. His mind is in the same condition as his fingers, working back to clods. He will get a rise of one and sixpence in a year or two, and marry on it and become duller and heavier; and, in short, the clever ones could already write his epitaph.

'A beautiful morning, Dering.'

'Too much sun, sir. The roses be complaining, and, to make matters worse, Miss

Barbara has been watering of them—in the heat of the day.'

The Colonel is a very gentle knight nowadays. 'Has she? She means well.' But that is not what is troubling him. He approaches the subject diffidently. 'Dering, you heard it, didn't you?' He is longing to be told that Dering heard it.

'What was that, sir?'

'The thunderstorm—early this morning.'

'There was no thunderstorm, sir.'

Dispirited, 'That is what they all say.' The Colonel is too courteous to contradict any one, but he tries again; there is about him the insistence of one who knows that he is right. 'It was at four o'clock. I got up and looked out at the window. The evening primroses were very beautiful.'

Dering is equally dogged. 'I don't hold much with evening primroses, sir; but I was out and about at four; there was no thunderstorm.'

The Colonel still thinks that there was a thunderstorm, but he wants to placate Dering.

'I suppose I just thought there was one. Perhaps it was some thunderstorm of long ago that I heard. They do come back, you know.'

Heavily, ' Do they, sir ? '

' I am glad to see you moving about in the garden, Dering, with everything just as usual.'

There is a cautious slyness about this, as if the Colonel was fishing for information; but it is too clever for Dering, who is going with a ' Thank you, sir.'

' No, don't go.' The old man lowers his voice and makes a confession reluctantly, ' I am—a little troubled, Dering.'

Dering knows that his master has a wandering mind, and he answers nicely, ' Everything be all right, sir.'

' I 'm glad of that,' the Colonel says with relief. ' It is pleasant to see that you have come back, Dering. Why did you go away for such a long time ? '

' Me, sir ? ' Dering is a little aggrieved. 'I haven't had a day off since Christmas.'

' Haven't you ?   I thought——'

The Colonel tries to speak casually, but

there is a trembling eagerness in his voice.
' Is everything just as usual, Dering ? '

' Yes, sir. There never were a place as
changed less than this.'

' That 's true.' The Colonel is appeased.
' Thank you, Dering, for saying that.' But
next moment he has lowered his voice again.
' Dering, there is nothing wrong, is there ?
Is anything happening that I am not being
told about ? '

' Not that I know of, sir.'

' That is what they all say, but—I don't
know.' He stares at his old sword which is
hanging on the wall. ' Dering, I feel as if I
was needed somewhere. I don't know where it
is. No one will tell me. Where is every one ? '

' They 're all about, sir. There 's a cricket
match on at the village green.'

' Is there ? '

' If the wind had a bit of south in it you
could hear their voices. You were a bit of a
nailer at cricket yourself, sir.'

The Colonel sees himself standing up to
fast ones. He is gleeful over his reminiscences.

' Ninety-nine against Mallowfield, and then bowled off my pads. Biggest score I ever made. Mallowfield wanted to add one to make it the hundred, but I wouldn't let them. I was pretty good at steering them through the slips, Dering! Do you remember my late cut? It didn't matter where point stood, I got past him. You used to stand at point, Dering.'

' That was my grandfather, sir. If he was to be believed, he used to snap you regular at point.'

The Colonel is crestfallen, but he has a disarming smile. ' Did he? I daresay he did. I can't play now, but I like to watch it still.' He becomes troubled again. ' Dering, there 's no cricket on the green to-day. I have been down to look. I don't understand it, Dering. When I got there the green was all dotted with them—it 's the prettiest sight and sound in England. But as I watched them they began to go away, one and two at a time; they weren't given out, you know, they went as if they had been called away. Some of the little shavers stayed on—and then they went off, as if they had been called away too. The stumps were left lying about. Why is it ? '

' It 's just fancy, sir,' Dering says soothingly. ' I saw Master Will oiling his bat yesterday.'

' Did you ? ' avidly. ' I should have liked to see that. I have often oiled their bats for them. Careless lads, they always forget. Was that nice German boy with him ? '

' Mr. Karl ? Not far off, sir. He was sitting by the bank of the stream playing on his flute ; and Miss Barbara, she had climbed one of my apple-trees,—she says they are your trees.' He lowers.

' They are, you know, Dering,' the Colonel says meekly.

' Yes, sir, in a sense,' brushing the spurious argument aside, ' but I don't like any of you to meddle with them. And there she sat, pelting the two of them with green apples.'

' How like her ! ' The Colonel shakes his

head indulgently. 'I don't know how we are to make a demure young lady of her.'

Dering smirks. 'They say in the village, sir, that Master Will would like to try.'

To the Colonel this is wit of a high order.

'Ha! ha! he is just a colt himself.' But the laughter breaks off. He seems to think that he will get the truth if Dering comes closer. 'Who are all here now, Dering; in the house, I mean? I sometimes forget. They grow old so quickly. They go out at one door in the bloom of youth, and come back by another, tired and grey. Haven't you noticed it?'

'No, sir. The only visitors staying here are Miss Barbara and Mr. Karl. There's just them and yourselves, sir, you and the mistress and Master Will. That's all.'

'Yes, that's all,' his master says, still unconvinced. 'Who is the soldier, Dering?'

'Soldier, sir? There is no soldier here except yourself.'

'Isn't there? There was a nurse with him. Who is ill?'

'No one, sir. There's no nurse.' Dering backs away from the old man. 'Would you like me to call the mistress, sir?'

'No, she has gone down to the village. She told me why, but I forget. Miss Barbara is with her.'

'Miss Barbara is down by the stream, sir.'

'Is she? I think they said they were going to a wedding.' With an old man's curiosity, 'Who is being married to-day, Dering?'

'I have heard of no wedding, sir. But here is Miss Barbara.'

It is perhaps the first time that Dering has been glad to see Miss Barbara, who romps in, a merry hoyden, running over with animal spirits.

'Here's the tomboy!' the Colonel cries gaily.

Barbara looks suspiciously from one to the other.

'Dering, I believe you are complaining to the Colonel about my watering the flowers at the wrong time of day.'

' Aha ! Aha ! ' The Colonel thinks she is
even wittier than Dering, who is properly
abashed.

' I did just mention it, miss.'

' You horrid ! ' Barbara shakes her mop
of hair at the gardener. ' Dear, don't mind
him. And every time he says they are *his*
flowers and *his* apples, you tell me, and I shall
say to his face that they are *yours*.'

' The courage of those young things ! ' says
the happy Colonel.

Dering's underlip becomes very pronounced,
but he goes off into the garden. Barbara
attempts to attend to the Colonel's needs.

' Let me make you comfy—the way granny
does it.'

She arranges his cushions clumsily.

' That is not quite the way she does it,' the
Colonel says softly. ' Do you call her
granny, Barbara ? '

' She asked me to—for practice.' Barbara
is curious. ' Don't you remember why ? '

Of course the Colonel remembers.

' I know ! Billy boy.'

'You *are* quick to-day. Now, wait till I get your cane.'

'I don't need my cane while I 'm sitting.'

'You look so beau'ful, sitting holding your cane.' She knocks over his cushions. 'Oh dear ! I am a clumsy.'

Politely, 'Not at all, but perhaps if I were to do it for myself.' He makes himself comfortable. 'That 's better. Thank you, Barbara, very much.'

'*I* didn't do it. I 'm all thumbs. What a ghastly nurse I should make.'

'Nurse ? ' The Colonel's troubles return to him. 'Who is she, Barbara ? '

'Who is who, dear ? '

'That nurse ? '

'There 's no nurse here.'

'Isn't there ? '

Barbara feels that she is of less use than ever to-day. 'Where is granny ? '

'She has gone down to the village to a wedding.'

'There 's no wedding. Who could be being married ? '

'I think it's people I know, but I can't remember who they are. I thought you went too, Barbara.'

'Not I. Catch me missing it if there had been a wedding!'

'You and the nurse.'

'Dear, you have just been imagining things again. Shall I play to you, or sing?' She knocks over a chair. 'Oh dear, everything catches in me. Would you like me to sing "Robin Adair," dear?'

The Colonel is polite, but firm. 'No, thank you, Barbara.' For a few moments he forgets her; his mind has gone wandering again. 'Barbara, the house seems so empty. Where are Billy and Karl?'

'Billy is where Karl is, you may be sure.'

'And where is Karl?'

'He is where Billy boy is, you may be sure.'

'And where are they both?'

'Not far from where Barbara is, you bet.' She flutters to the window and waves her hand. 'Do you hear Karl's flute? They

have been down all the morning at the pool
where the alder is, trying to catch that bull-
trout.'

'They didn't get him, I'll swear!'

'You can ask them.'

'I spent a lot of my youth trying to get
that bull-trout. I tumbled in there sixty
years ago.'

'I tumbled in sixty minutes ago! It can't
be the same trout, dear.'

'Same old rascal!'

Billy and Karl come in by the window,
leaving a fishing-rod outside. They are gay,
careless, attractive youths.

BARBARA, with her nose in the air, 'You
muddy things!'

COLONEL, gaily firing his dart, 'Did you get
the bull-trout, Billy boy?'

BILLY.   'He's a brute that.'

COLONEL.   'He is, you know.'

BILLY.   'He came up several times and had a
look at my fly. Didn't flick it, or do anything as complimentary as that. Just yawned
and went down.'

COLONEL. 'Yawned, did he? Used to wink in my time. Did you and Billy fish at Heidelberg, Karl?'

KARL. 'We were more worthily employed, sir, but we did unbend at times. Billy, do you remember——' He begins a gay dance.

BILLY. 'Not I.' Then he joins in.

BARBARA. 'Young gentlemen, how disgraceful!' She joins in.

COLONEL. 'Harum-scarums!'

KARL. 'Does he know about you two?'

BILLY. 'He often forgets. I'll tell him again. Grandfather, Barbara and I have something to say to you. It's this.' He puts his arm round Barbara.

COLONEL, smiling, 'I know—I know. There's nothing like it. I'm very glad, Barbara.'

BARBARA. 'You see, dear, I've loved Billy boy since the days when he tried to catch the bull-trout with a string and a bent pin, and I held on to his pinafore to prevent his tumbling in. We used to play at school at marrying and giving in marriage, and the girl who was my bridegroom had always to take the name of Billy. " Do you, woman, take this man Billy——" the clergyman in skirts began, and before I could answer diffidently, some other girl was sure to shout, " I should rather think she does." '

COLONEL, in high good humour, ' Don't forget the ring, Billy. You know, when I was married I think I couldn't find the ring ! '

KARL.   ' Were you married here, sir ? '

COLONEL.   ' Yes, at the village church.'

BILLY.   ' So were my father and mother.'

COLONEL, as his eyes wander to the garden, ' I remember walking back with my wife and bringing her in here through the window. She kissed some of the furniture.'

BILLY.   ' I suppose you would like a grander affair, Barbara ? '

BARBARA.   ' No, just the same.'

BILLY.   ' I hoped you would say that.'

BARBARA.   ' But, Billy, I'm to have such a dream of a wedding gown.   Granny is going with me to London to choose it '—laying her head on the Colonel's shoulder—' if you can do without her for a day, dear.'

COLONEL, gallantly, 'I shall go with you. I couldn't trust you and granny to choose the gown.'

KARL. 'You must often be pretty lonely, sir, when we are all out and about enjoying ourselves.'

COLONEL. 'They all say that. But that is the time when I 'm not lonely, Karl. It 's then I see things most clearly—the past, I suppose. It all comes crowding back to me—India, the Crimea, India again—and it 's so real, especially the people. They come and talk to me. I seem to see them; I don't know they haven't been here, Billy, till your granny tells me afterwards.'

BILLY. 'Yes, I know. I wonder where granny is.'

BARBARA. 'It isn't often she leaves you for so long, dear.'

COLONEL. 'She told me she had to go out, but I forget where. Oh, yes, she has gone down to the village to a wedding.'

BILLY. 'A wedding ? '

BARBARA. 'It 's curious how he harps on that.'

COLONEL. 'She said to me to listen and I would hear the wedding bells.'

BARBARA. 'Not to-day, dear.'

BILLY. 'Best not to worry him.'

BARBARA. 'But granny says we should try to make things clear to him.'

BILLY. 'Was any one with granny when she said she was going to a wedding?'

COLONEL, like one begging her to admit it, 'You were there, Barbara.'

BARBARA. 'No, dear. He said that to me before. And something about a nurse.'

COLONEL, obstinately, 'She was there, too.'

BILLY. 'Any one else?'

COLONEL. 'There was that soldier.'

BARBARA. 'A soldier also!'

COLONEL. 'Just those three.'

BILLY. 'But that makes four. Granny and Barbara and a nurse and a soldier.'

COLONEL. 'They were all there; but there were only three.'

BILLY. 'Odd.'

BARBARA, soothingly, 'Never mind, dear.

Granny will make it all right. She is the one for you.'

COLONEL. ' She is the one for me.'

KARL. ' If there had been a wedding, wouldn't she have taken the Colonel with her ? '

BARBARA. ' Of course she would.'

KARL. ' You are not too old to have a kind eye for a wedding, sir.'

COLONEL, wagging his head, ' Aha, aha ! You know, if I had gone, very likely I should have kissed the bride. Brides look so pretty on their wedding day. They are often not pretty at other times, but they are all pretty on their wedding day.'

KARL. ' You have an eye for a pretty girl still, sir !'

COLONEL. ' Yes, I have ; yes, I have ! '

BARBARA. ' I do believe I see it all. Granny has been talking to you about Billy boy and me, and you haven't been able to wait ; you have hurried on the wedding !'

BILLY. ' Bravo, Barbara, you 've got it.'

COLONEL, doubtfully, ' That may be it. Because I am sure you were to be there, Barbara.'

BARBARA. ' Our wedding, Billy !'

H

KARL.   ' It doesn't explain those other people, though.'

The Colonel moves about in agitation.

BARBARA.   ' What is it, dear ? '

COLONEL.   ' I can't quite remember, but I think that is why she didn't take me. It is your wedding, Barbara, but I don't think Billy boy is to be there, my love.'

BARBARA.   ' Not at my wedding ! '

BILLY.   ' Grandfather ! '

COLONEL.   ' There 's something sad about it.'

BARBARA.   ' There can't be anything sad about a wedding, dear. Granny didn't say it was a sad wedding, did she ? '

COLONEL.   ' She was smiling.'

BARBARA.   ' Of course she was.'

COLONEL.   ' But I think that was only to please the nurse.'

BARBARA.   ' That nurse again ! Dear, don't think any more about it. There 's no wedding.'

COLONEL, gently, though he wonders why they can go on deceiving him, ' Is there not ? '

The village wedding bells begin to ring.

The Colonel is triumphant. ' I told you !
There is a wedding ! '

The bells ring on gaily. Billy and Barbara
take a step nearer to each other, but can go
no closer. The bells ring on, and the three
young people fade from the scene.

When they are gone and he is alone,
the Colonel still addresses them. ' It 's
Barbara's wedding. Billy boy, why are you
not at Barbara's wedding ? '

Soon the bells stop. He knows that he is
alone now, but he does not understand it.
The sun is shining brightly, but he sits very
cold in his chair. He shivers. He is very
glad to see his wife coming to him through
the open window. She is a dear old lady,
and is dressed brightly, as becomes one who
has been to a wedding. Her face beams to
match her gown. She is really quite a happy
woman again, for it is several years since
any deep sorrow struck her; and that is a
long time. No one, you know, understands
the Colonel as she does, no one can soothe
him and bring him out of his imaginings as

she can.   He hastens to her.   He is no longer
cold.   That is her great reward for all she
does for him.

'I have come back, John,' she says, smiling
tranquilly on him.   'It hasn't seemed very
long, has it ? '

'No, not long, Ellen.   Had you a nice
walk ? '

She continues to smile, but she is watching
him closely.   'I haven't been for a walk.
Don't you remember where I told you I was
going, John ? '

'Yes, it was to a wedding.'

Rather tremulously, ' You haven't forgotten
whose wedding, have you ? '

'Tell me, Ellen.'   He is no longer troubled.
He knows that Ellen will tell him.

'I have been seeing Barbara married,
John.'

'Yes, it was Barbara's wedding.   They
wouldn't—— Ellen, why wasn't I there ? '

Like one telling him amusing gossip, ' I
thought you might be a little troubled if you
went, John.   Sometimes your mind—not

often, but sometimes if you are agitated—
and then you think you see—people who
aren't here any longer. Oh dear, oh dear,
help me with these bonnet strings.'

'Yes, I know. I 'm all right when you are
with me, Ellen. Funny, isn't it ? '

She raises her shoulders in a laugh. 'It *is*
funny, John. I ran back to you, John. I
was thinking of you all the time—even more
than of Billy boy.'

The Colonel is very gay. 'Tell me all
about it, Ellen. Did Billy boy lose the ring ?
We always said he would lose the ring.'

She looks straight into his eyes. 'You
have forgotten again, John. Barbara isn't
married to Billy boy.'

He draws himself up. 'Not marry Billy !
I 'll see about that.'

She presses him into his chair. 'Sit down,
dear, and I 'll tell you something again. It is
nothing to trouble you, because your soldier-
ing is done, John; and greatly done. My
dear, there is war again, and our old land is
in it. Such a war as my soldier never knew.'

He rises. He is a stern old man. 'A war! That's it, is it? So now I know! Why wasn't I told? Why haven't I my marching orders? I'm not too old yet.'

'Yes, John, you are too old, and all you can do now is to sit here and—and take care of me. You knew all about it quite clearly this morning. We stood together upstairs by the window listening to the aircraft guns.'

'I remember! I thought it was a thunderstorm. Dering told me he heard nothing.'

'Dering?'

'Our gardener, you know.' His voice becomes husky. 'Haven't I been talking with him, Ellen?'

'It is a long time since we had a gardener, John.'

'Is it? So it is! A war! That is why there is no more cricket on the green.'

'They have all gone to the war, John.'

'That's it; even the little shavers.' He whispers, 'Why isn't Billy boy fighting, Ellen?'

' Oh, John ! '

' Is Billy boy dead ? ' She nods. ' Was he killed in action ? Tell me, tell me ! ' She nods again. ' Good for Billy boy. I knew Billy boy was all right. Don't cry, Ellen. I 'll take care of you. All 's well with Billy boy.'

' Yes, I know, John.'

He hesitates before speaking again. ' Ellen, who is the soldier ? He comes here. He is a captain.'

' He is a very gallant man, John. It is he who was married to Barbara to-day.'

Bitterly, ' She has soon forgotten.'

His wife shakes her brave head. ' She hasn't forgotten, dear. And it 's nearly three years now since Billy died.'

' So long ! We have a medal he got, haven't we ? '

' No, John ; he died before he could win any medals.'

The Colonel moves about, ' Karl will be sorry. They were very fond of each other, those two boys, Ellen.'

' Karl fought against us, John. He died in the same engagement. They may even have killed each other.'

' They hadn't known, Ellen.'

She says with thin lips, ' I daresay they knew.'

' Billy boy and Karl ! '

She tells him some more gossip. ' John, I had Barbara married from here because she has no people of her own. I think Billy would have liked it.'

' That was the thing to do, Ellen. Nice of you. I remember everything now. It 's Dering she has married. He was once my gardener ! '

' The world is all being re-made, dear. He is worthy of her.'

He lets this pass. He has remembered something almost as surprising. ' Ellen, is Barbara a nurse ? '

' Yes, John, and one of the staidest and most serene. Who would have thought it of the merry madcap of other days ! They are coming here, John, to say good-bye to you.

They have only a few days' leave. She is
in France, too, you know. She was married
in her nurse's uniform.'

' Was she ? She told me to-day that—no,
it couldn't have been to-day.'

' You have been fancying you saw them,
I suppose.' She grows tremulous again. 'You
will be nice to them, John, won't you, and
wish them luck ? They have their trials
before them.'

He says eagerly, ' Tell me what to do,
Ellen.'

' Don't say anything about Billy boy,
John.'

' No no, let 's pretend.'

' And I wouldn't talk about the garden,
John ; just in case he is a little touchy about
that.'

The Colonel is beginning to fancy himself
as a tactician. ' Not a word ! '

She knows what is the way to put him
on his mettle. ' You see, I 'm sure I would
make a mess of it, so I 'm trusting to you,
John.'

He is very pleased. 'Leave it all to me, Ellen. I'll be frightfully sly. You just watch me.'

She goes to the window and calls to the married couple. Captain Dering, in khaki, is a fine soldierly figure. Barbara, in her Red Cross uniform, is quiet and resourceful. An artful old boy greets them. 'Congratulations, Barbara. No, no, none of your handshaking; you don't get past an old soldier in that way. Excuse me, young man.' He kisses Barbara and looks at his wife to make sure that she is admiring him. 'And to you, Captain Dering—you have won a prize.'

A gallant gentleman answers, 'I know it; I'll try to show I know it.'

The Colonel is perturbed. 'I haven't given Barbara a wedding present, Ellen. I should like——'

Barbara breaks in, 'Indeed you have, dear, and a lovely one. You haven't forgotten?'

Granny signs to the Colonel and he immedi-

ately says, with remarkable cunning, ' Oh
—that! I was just quizzing you, Barbara.
I hope you will be as happy, dear, staid
Barbara, as if you had married——' He sees
that he has nearly given away the situation.
He looks triumphantly at granny as much
as to say, ' Observe me; I'm not going to
say a word about him.'

Granny comes to his aid. ' Perhaps
Captain Dering has some little things to do:
and you, too, Barbara. They are leaving in
an hour, John.'

For a moment the Colonel is again in
danger. ' If you would like to take Barbara
into the garden, Captain Dering——' He
recovers himself instantly. ' No, not the
garden, you wouldn't know your way about
in the garden.'

' Wouldn't I, Colonel?' the captain says,
smiling.

The answer is quite decisive. 'No, certainly
not. I'll show it you some day.' He makes
gleeful signs to granny. ' But there is a nice
meadow just beyond the shrubbery. Barbara

knows the way; she often went there with——'
He checks himself. Granny signs to them to
go, and Barbara kisses both the Colonel's
hands. 'The Captain will be jealous, you
know,' he says, twinkling.

'Let me, dear,' says Barbara, arranging
his cushions professionally.

Granny nods. 'She is much better at it
than I am now, John.'

The Colonel has one last piece of advice to
give. 'I wouldn't go down by the stream,
Barbara—not to the pool where the alder is.
There's—there's not a good view there, sir;
and a boy—a boy I knew, he often—nobody
in particular—just a boy who used to come
about the house—he is not here now—he is
on duty. I don't think you should go to the
alder pool, Barbara.'

'We won't go there, dear.' She and her
husband go out, and the Colonel scarcely
misses them, he is so eager to hear what his
wife thinks of him.

'Did I do all right, Ellen?'

'Splendidly. I was proud of you.'

He exults. ' I put them completely off the scent ! They haven't a notion ! I can be very sly, you know, at times. Ellen, I think I should like to have that alder tree cut down. There is no boy now, you see.'

' I would leave it alone, John. There will be boys again. Shall I read to you ; you like that, don't you ? '

' Yes, read to me—something funny, if you please. About Sam Weller ! No, I expect Sam has gone to the wars. Read about Mr. Pickwick. He is very amusing. I feel sure that if he had tried to catch the bull-trout he would have fallen in. Just as Barbara did this morning.'

' Barbara ? '

' She is down at the alder pool. Billy is there with that nice German boy. The noise they make, shouting and laughing ! '

She gets from its shelf the best book for war-time. ' Which bit shall I read ? '

' About Mr. Pickwick going into the lady's bedroom by mistake.'

' Yes, dear, though you almost know it by

heart.   You see, you have begun to laugh
already.'

' You are laughing too, Ellen.   I can't help
it ! '

She begins to read ; they are both chuckling.

A WELL-REMEMBERED VOICE

Out of the darkness comes the voice of a woman speaking to her dead son.

' But that was against your wish, was it not ? Was that against your wish ?   Would you prefer me not to ask that question ? '

The room is so dark that we cannot see her. All we know is that she is one of four shapes gathered round a small table.   Beyond the darkness is a great ingle-nook, in which is seated on a settle a man of fifty.   Him we can discern fitfully by the light of the fire.   It is not sufficiently bright to enable him to read, but an evening paper lies on his knee.   He seems wistful and meek.   He is paying no attention to the party round the table.   When he hears their voices it is only as empty sounds.

The mother continues.   ' Perhaps I am putting the question in the wrong way.   Are you not able to tell us any more ? '

A man's voice breaks in. 'There was a distinct movement that time, but it is so irregular.'

'I thought so, but please don't talk. Do you want to tell us more? Is it that you can't hear me distinctly? He seems to want to tell us more, but something prevents him.'

'In any case, Mrs. Don, it is extraordinary. This is the first séance I have ever taken part in, but I must believe now.'

'Of course, Major, these are the simplest manifestations. They are only the first step. But if we are to go on, the less we talk the better. Shall we go on? It is not agitating you too much, Laura?'

A girl answers. 'There was a moment when I—but I wish I was braver. I think it is partly the darkness. I suppose we can't have a little light?'

'Certainly we can, dear. Darkness is quite unnecessary, but I think it helps one to concentrate.'

The Major lights a lamp, and though it casts shadows we see now that the room is an artist's studio. The silent figure in the ingle-nook is the artist. Mrs. Don is his wife, the two men are Major Armitage and an older friend, Mr. Rogers. The girl is Laura Bell. These four are sitting round the table, their hands touching : they are endeavouring to commune with one who has ' crossed the gulf.'

The Major and Mr. Rogers are but passing shadows in the play, and even nice Laura is only to flit across its few pages for a moment on her way to happier things. We scarcely notice them in the presence of Mrs. Don, the gracious, the beautiful, the sympathetic, whose magnetic force and charm are such that we wish to sit at her feet at once. She is intellectual, but with a disarming smile, religious, but so charitable, masterful, and yet loved of all. None is perfect, and there must be a flaw in her somewhere, but to find it would necessitate such a rummage among her many adornments as there is now no time for. Perhaps we may come upon it accidentally in the course of the play.

She is younger than Mr. Don, who, despite her efforts for many years to cover his deficiencies, is a man of no great account in a household where the bigger personality of his wife swallows him like an Aaron's rod. Mr. Don's deficiencies! She used to try very hard, or fairly hard, to conceal them from Dick; but Dick knew. His mother was his chum. All the lovely things which happened in that house in the days when Dick was alive were between him and her; those two shut the door softly on old Don, always anxious not to hurt his feelings, and then ran into each other's arms.

In the better light Mr. Don is now able to read his paper if he chooses. If he has forgotten the party at the table, they have equally forgotten him.

MRS. DON. 'You have not gone away, have you? We must be patient. Are you still there?'

ROGERS. 'I think I felt a movement.'

MRS. DON. 'Don't talk, please. Are you still there?'

The table moves.

'Yes! It is your mother who is speaking; do you understand that?'

The table moves.

' Yes.   What shall I ask him now ? '

ROGERS.   ' We leave it to you, Mrs. Don.'

MRS. DON.   ' Have you any message you want to send us ?   Yes.   Is it important ?   Yes. Are we to spell it out in the usual way ? Yes.   Is the first letter of the first word A ? Is it B ? '

She continues through the alphabet to L, when the table responds.   Similarly she finds that the second letter is O.

' Is the word *Love* ?   Yes.   But I don't understand that movement.   You are not displeased with us, are you ?   No.   Does the second word begin with A ?—with B ?   Yes.'

The second word is spelt out *Bade* and the third *Me*.

' Love Bade Me——   If it is a quotation, I believe I know it !   Is the fourth word *Welcome* ?   Yes.'

LAURA.   ' Love Bade Me Welcome.'

MRS. DON.   ' That movement again !   Don't you want me to go on ? '

LAURA.   ' Let us stop.'

MRS. DON. ' Not unless he wishes it. Why are those words so important ? Does the message end there ? Is any one working against you ? Some one antagonistic ? Yes. Not one of ourselves surely ? No. Is it any one we know ? Yes. Can I get the name in the usual way ? Yes. Is the first letter of this person's name A ?—B ?——'

It proves to be F. One begins to notice a quaint peculiarity of Mrs. Don's. She is so accustomed to homage that she expects a prompt response even from the shades.

' Is the second letter A ? '

The table moves.

' FA. Fa—— ? '

She is suddenly enlightened.

' Is the word Father ? Yes.'

They all turn and look for the first time at Mr. Don. He has heard, and rises apologetically.

MR. DON, distressed, ' I had no intention—— Should I go away, Grace ? '

She answers sweetly without a trace of the annoyance she must surely feel.

MRS. DON.   ' Perhaps you had better, Robert.'

ROGERS.   ' I suppose it is because he is an un-
believer ?   He is not openly antagonistic, is
he ? '

MRS. DON, sadly enough, ' I am afraid he is.'

They tend to discuss the criminal as if he
was not present.

MAJOR.   ' But he must admit that we do get
messages.'

MRS. DON, reluctantly, ' He says we think we
do.   He says they would not want to com-
municate with us if they had such trivial
things to say.'

ROGERS.   ' But we are only on the threshold,
Don.   This is just a beginning.'

LAURA.   ' Didn't you hear, Mr. Don—" Love
Bade Me Welcome " ? '

MR. DON.   ' Does that strike you as important,
Laura ? '

LAURA.   ' He said it was.'

MRS. DON.   ' It might be very important to
him, though we don't understand why.'

She speaks gently, but there is an obstinacy
in him, despite his meekness.

MR. DON. ' I didn't mean to be antagonistic, Grace. I thought. I wasn't thinking of it at all.'

MRS. DON. ' Not thinking of Dick, Robert ? And it was only five months ago ! '

MR. DON, who is somehow, without meaning it, always in the wrong, ' I 'll go.'

ROGERS. ' A boy wouldn't turn his father out. Ask him.'

MR. DON, forlornly, ' As to that — as to that——'

MRS. DON. ' I will ask him if you wish me to, Robert.'

MR. DON. ' No, don't.'

ROGERS. ' It can't worry you as you are a disbeliever.'

MR. DON. ' No, but—I shouldn't like you to think that he sent me away.'

ROGERS. ' He won't. Will he, Mrs. Don ? '

MR. DON, knowing what her silence implies, ' You see, Dick and I were not very—no quarrel or anything of that sort—but I, I didn't much matter to Dick. I 'm too old, perhaps.'

MRS. DON, gently, 'I won't ask him, Robert, if you would prefer me not to.'

MR. DON. 'I'll go.'

MRS. DON. 'I'm afraid it is too late now.' She turns away from earthly things. 'Do you want me to break off ?'

The table moves.

'Yes. Do you send me your love, Dick ? Yes. And to Laura ? Yes.' She raises her eyes to Don, and hesitates. 'Shall I ask him—— ?'

MR. DON. 'No, no, don't.'

ROGERS. 'It would be all right, Don.'

MR. DON. 'I don't know.'

They leave the table.

LAURA, a little agitated, 'May I go to my room, Mrs. Don ? I feel I—should like to be alone.'

MRS. DON. 'Yes, yes, Laura dear. I shall come in and see you.'

Laura bids them good-night and goes. She likes Mr. Don, she strokes his hand when he holds it out to her, but she can't help saying, 'Oh, Mr. Don, how could you ?'

ROGERS. ' I think we must all want to be alone after such an evening. I shall say good-night, Mrs. Don.'

MAJOR. ' Same here. I go your way, Rogers, but you will find me a silent companion. One doesn't want to talk ordinary things to-night. Rather not. Thanks, awfully.'

ROGERS. ' Good-night, Don. It 's a pity, you know ; a bit hard on your wife.'

MR. DON. ' Good-night, Rogers. Good-night, Major.'

The husband and wife, left together, have not much to say to each other. He is depressed because he has spoilt things for her. She is not angry. She knows that he can't help being as he is, and that there are fine spaces in her mind where his thoughts can never walk with hers. But she would forgive him seventy times seven because he is her husband. She is standing looking at a case of fishing-rods against the wall. There is a Jock Scott still sticking in one of them. Mr. Don says, as if somehow they were evidence against him ;

'Dick's fishing-rods.'

She says forgivingly, 'I hope you don't mind my keeping them in the studio, Robert. They are sacred things to *me*.'

'That's all right, Grace.'

'I think I shall go to Laura now.'

'Yes,' in his inexpressive way.

'Poor child!'

'I'm afraid I hurt her.'

'Dick wouldn't have liked it—but Dick's gone.' She looks a little wonderingly at him. After all these years, she can sometimes wonder a little still. 'I suppose you will resume your evening paper!'

He answers quietly, but with the noble doggedness which is the reason why we write this chapter in his life. 'Why not, Grace?'

She considers, for she is so sure that she must know the answer better than he. 'I suppose it is just that a son is so much more to a mother than to a father.'

'I daresay.'

A little gust of passion shakes her. 'How you can read about the war nowadays!'

He says firmly to her—he has had to
say it a good many times to himself, ' I 'm
not going to give in.' But he adds, ' I
am so sorry I was in the way, Grace.
I wasn't scouting you, or anything of
that sort. It 's just that I can't believe
in it.'

' Ah, Robert, you would believe if Dick
had been to you what he was to me.'

' I don't know.'

' In a sense you may be glad that you
don't miss him in the way I do.'

' Yes, perhaps.'

' Good-night, Robert.'

' Good-night, dear.'

He is alone now. He stands fingering
the fishing-rods tenderly, then wanders back
into the ingle-nook. In the room we could
scarcely see him, for it has gone slowly dark
there, a grey darkness, as if the lamp, though
still burning, was becoming unable to shed
light. Through the greyness we see him
very well beyond it in the glow of the fire.
He sits on the settle and tries to read his

paper. He breaks down. He is a pitiful lonely man.

In the silence something happens. A well-remembered voice says, ' Father.' Mr. Don looks into the greyness from which this voice comes, and he sees his son. We see no one, but we are to understand that, to Mr, Don, Dick is standing there in his habit as he lived. He goes to his boy.

' Dick ! '

' I have come to sit with you for a bit, father.'

It is the gay, young, careless voice.

' It 's you, Dick; it 's you ! '

' It 's me all right, father. I say, don't be startled, or anything of that kind. We don't like that.'

' My boy ! '

Evidently Dick is the taller, for Mr. Don has to look up to him. He puts his hands on the boy's shoulders.

' How am I looking, father ? '

' You haven't altered, Dick.'

' Rather not. It 's jolly to see the old

studio again ! ' In a cajoling voice, ' I say, father, don't fuss. Let us be our ordinary selves, won't you ? '

' I 'll try, I 'll try. You didn't say you had come to sit with *me*, Dick ? Not with *me* ! '

' Rather ! '

' But your mother——'

' It 's you I want.'

' Me ? '

' We can only come to one, you see.'

' Then why me ? '

' That 's the reason.' He is evidently moving about, looking curiously at old acquaintances. ' Hello, here 's your old jacket, greasier than ever ! '

' Me ? But, Dick, it is as if you had forgotten. It was your mother who was everything to you. It can't be you if you have forgotten that. I used to feel so out of it ; but, of course, you didn't know.'

' I didn't know it till lately, father ; but heaps of things that I didn't know once are clear to me now. I didn't know that you

were the one who would miss me most; but
I know now.'

Though the voice is as boyish as ever,
there is a new note in it of which his father
is aware. Dick may not have grown much
wiser, but whatever he does know now he
seems to know for certain.

' *Me* miss you most ? Dick, I try to paint
just as before. I go to the club. Dick, I
have been to a dinner-party. I said I
wouldn't give in.'

' We like that.'

' But, my boy——'

Mr. Don's arms have gone out to him again.
Dick evidently wriggles away from them.
He speaks coaxingly.

' I say, father, let's get away from that
sort of thing.'

' That is so like you, Dick ! I 'll do anything you ask.'

' Then keep a bright face.'

' I 've tried to.'

' Good man ! I say, put on your old
greasy ; you are looking so beastly clean.'

The old greasy is the jacket, and Mr. Don obediently gets into it.

' Anything you like.   No, that 's the wrong sleeve.   Thanks, Dick.'

They are in the ingle-nook now, and the mischievous boy catches his father by the shoulders.

' Here, let me shove you into your old seat.'

Mr. Don is propelled on to the settle.

' How 's that, umpire ! '

' Dick,' smiling, ' that 's just how you used to butt me into it long ago ! '

Dick is probably standing with his back to the fire, chuckling.

' When I was a kid.'

' With the palette in my hand.'

' Or sticking to your trousers.'

' The mess we made of ourselves, Dick.'

' I sneaked behind the settle and climbed up it.'

' Till you fell off.'

' On top of you and the palette.'

It is good fun for a father and son ; and the

crafty boy has succeeded in making the father laugh. But soon,

' Ah, Dick.'

The son frowns. He is not going to stand any nonsense.

' Now then, behave ! What did I say about that face ? '

Mr. Don smiles at once, obediently.

' That 's better. I 'll sit here.'

We see from his father's face which is smiling with difficulty that Dick has plopped into the big chair on the other side of the inglenook. His legs are probably dangling over one of its arms.

Rather sharply, ' Got your pipe ? '

' I don't—I don't seem to care to smoke nowadays, Dick.'

' Rot ! Just because I am dead ! You that pretend to be plucky ! I won't have it, you know. You get your pipe, and look slippy about it.'

' Yes, Dick,' the old man says obediently. He fills his pipe from a jar on the mantelshelf. We may be sure that Dick is watching closely to see that he lights it properly.

'Now, then, burn your thumb with the match—you always did, you know. That's the style. You've forgotten to cock your head to the side. Not so bad. That's you. Like it?'

'It's rather nice, Dick. Dick, you and me by the fire!'

'Yes, but sit still. How often we might have been like this, father, and weren't.'

'Ah!'

'Face. How is Fido?'

'Never a dog missed her master more.'

'Oh,' frowning. 'She doesn't want to go and sit on my grave, or any of that tosh, does she? As if I were there!'

'No, no,' hastily; 'she goes ratting, Dick.'

'Good old Fido!'

'Dick, here's a good one. We oughtn't to keep a dog at all because we are on rations now; but what do you think Fido ate yesterday?'

'Let me guess. The joint?'

'Almost worse than that. She ate all the cook's meat tickets.'

They laugh together, but when Dick says light-heartedly, 'That dog will be the death of me,' his father shivers. Dick does not notice this; his eyes have drawn him to the fishing-rods.

'Hullo!'

'Yes, those are your old fishing-rods.'

'Here's the little hickory! Do you remember, father, how I got the seven-pounder on a burn-trout cast? No, you weren't there. That was a day. It was really only six and three-quarters. I put a stone in its mouth the second time we weighed it!'

'You loved fishing, Dick.'

'Didn't I? Why weren't you oftener with me? I'll tell you a funny thing. When I went a-soldiering I used to pray—just standing up, you know—that I shouldn't lose my right arm, because it would be so awkward for casting.' He cogitates as he returns to the ingle-nook. 'Somehow I never thought I should be killed. Lots of fellows thought

K

that about themselves, but I never did.   It
was quite a surprise to me.'

' Oh, Dick ! '

' What 's the matter ?   Oh, I forgot.
Face ! '   He is apparently looking down at
his father wonderingly.   Haven't you got
over it yet, father ?   I got over it so long
ago.   I wish you people would understand
what a little thing it is.'

' Tell me,' very humbly ; ' tell me, Dick.'

' All right.'   He is in the chair again.
' Mind, I can't tell you where I was killed ;
it 's against the regulations.'

' I know where.'

Curiously, ' You got a wire, I suppose ? '

' Yes.'

' There 's always a wire for officers, even
for 2nd Lieutenants.   It 's jolly decent of
them.'

' Tell me, Dick, about the—the veil.   I
mean the veil that is drawn between the
living and the——'

' The dead ?   Funny how you jib at that
word.'

' I suppose the veil is like a mist ? '

' The veil 's a rummy thing, father. Yes, like a mist. But when one has been at the Front for a bit, you can't think how thin the veil seems to get; just one layer of it. I suppose it seems thin to you out there because one step takes you through it. We sometimes mix up those who have gone through with those who haven't. I daresay if I were to go back to my old battalion the living chaps would just nod to me.'

' Dick ! '

' Where 's that pipe ? Death ? Well, to me, before my day came, it was like some part of the line I had heard a lot about but never been in. I mean, never been in to stay, because, of course, one often popped in and out.'

' Dick, the day that you——'

' My day ? I don't remember being hit, you know. I don't remember anything till the quietness came. When you have been killed it suddenly becomes very quiet ; quieter even than you have ever known it

at home. Sunday used to be a pretty quiet
day at my tutors, when Trotter and I flattened
out on the first shady spot up the river ; but
it is quieter than that. I am not boring you,
am I ? '

' My boy ! '

' When I came to, the veil was so thin
that I couldn't see it at all ; and my first
thought was, Which side of it have I come
out on ? The living ones lying on the ground
were asking that about themselves, too.
There we were, all sitting up and asking
whether we were alive or dead ; and some
were one, and some were the other. Sort of
fluke, you know.'

' I—I—oh, Dick ! '

' As soon as each had found out about
himself he wondered how it had gone with his
chums. I halloo'd to Johnny Randall, and
he halloo'd back that he was dead, but that
Trotter was living. That's the way of it.
A good deal of chaff, of course. By that time
the veil was there, and getting thicker, and
we lined up on our right sides. Then I could

only see the living ones in shadow and hear
their voices from a distance. They sang out
to us for a while ; but just at first, father,
it was rather lonely when we couldn't hear
their tread any longer. What are you fid-
geting about ? You needn't worry ; that
didn't last long ; we were heaps more interested in ourselves than in them. You should
have heard the gabbling ! It was all so
frightfully novel, you see ; and no one quite
knew what to do next, whether all to start
off together, or wait for some one to come
for us. I say, what a lot I 'm talking ! '

' What happened, Dick ? '

' Oh ! ' a proud ring coming into the voice,
' Ockley came for us. He used to be alive,
you know—the Ockley who was keeper of the
fives in my first half. I once pointed him
out to mother. I was jolly glad he was the
one who came for us. As soon as I saw it
was Ockley I knew we should be all right.'

' Dick, I like that Ockley.'

' Rather. I wish I could remember something funny to tell you though. There are lots

of jokes, but I am such a one for forgetting them.'

He laughs boisterously. We may be sure that he flings back his head. You remember how Dick used to fling back his head when he laughed ?—No, you didn't know him.

'Father, do you remember little Wantage who was at my private and came on to Ridley's house in my third half ? His mother was the one you called Emily.'

'Emily Wantage's boy.'

'That's the card. We used to call him Jemima, because he and his mother were both caught crying when lock-up struck, and she had to clear out.'

'She was very fond of him, Dick.'

'Oh, I expect no end. Tell her he's killed.'

'She knows.'

'She had got a wire. That isn't the joke, though. You see he got into a hopeless muddle about which side of the veil he had come out on ; and he went off with the other ones, and they wouldn't have him, and he got lost in the veil, running up and down it, calling to us; and just for the lark we didn't answer.' He chuckles. 'I expect he has become a ghost!' With sudden consideration, 'Best not tell his mother that.'

Mr. Don rises, wincing, and Dick also is at once on his feet, full of compunction.

'Was that shabby of me? Sorry, father. We are all pretty young, you know, and we can't help having our fun still.'

'I'm glad you still have your fun,' the father says, once more putting his hands on Dick's shoulders. 'Let me look at you again, Dick. There is such a serenity about you now.'

'Serenity, that's the word! None of us could remember what the word was. It's a ripping good thing to have. I should be awfully bucked if you would have it, too.'

'I'll try.'

'I say, how my tongue runs on! But, after all, it was my show. Now, you tell me some things.'

'What about, Dick? The war?'

' No,' almost in a shout. ' We have a fine for speaking about the war. And you know, those fellows we were fighting—I forget who they were ? '

' The Germans.'

' Oh yes. Some of them were on the same side of the veil with us, and they were rather decent; so we chummed up in the end and Ockley took us all away together. They were jolly lucky in getting Ockley. There I go again ! Come on, it 's your turn. Has the bathroom tap been mended yet ? '

' I 'm afraid it is—just tied up with that string still, Dick. It works all right.'

' It only needs two screw-nails, you know.'

' I 'll see to it.'

' Do you know whether any one at my tutors got his fives choice this half ? '

' I 'm sorry, Dick, but——'

' Or who is the captain of the boats ? '

' No, I——'

' Whatever have you been doing ? ' He is moving about the room. ' Hullo, here 's mother's workbox ! Is mother all right ? '

' Very sad about you, Dick.'

' Oh, I say, that isn't fair. Why doesn't she cheer up ? '

' It isn't so easy, my boy.'

' It's pretty hard lines on me, you know.'

' How is that ? '

' If you are sad, I have to be sad. That's how we have got to work it off. You can't think how we want to be bright.'

' I'll always remember that, and I'll tell your mother. Ah, but she won't believe me, Dick ; you will have to tell her yourself.'

' I can't do that, father. I can only come to one.'

' She should have been the one ; she loved you best, Dick.'

' Oh, I don't know. Do you ever,' with a slight hesitation, ' see Laura now ? '

' She is staying with us at present.'

' Is she ? I think I should like to see her.'

' If Laura were to see you——'

' Oh, she wouldn't see me. She is not dressed in black, is she ? '

' No, in white.'

' Good girl ! I suppose mother is in black ? '

' Surely, Dick.'

' It 's too bad, you know.'

' You weren't exactly—engaged to Laura, were you, Dick ? ' A bold question from a father, but the circumstances were unusual. Apologetically, ' I never rightly knew.'

' No ! ' Dick has flung back his head again. Confidentially, ' Father, I sometimes thought of it, but it rather scared me ! I expect that is about how it was with her, too.'

' She is very broken about you now.'

Irritated, ' Oh, hang ! '

' Would you like her to forget you, Dick ? '

' Rather not. But she might help a fellow a bit. Hullo ! '

What calls forth this exclamation is the little table at which the séance had taken place. The four chairs are still standing round it, as if they were guarding something.

' Here 's something new, father ; this table.'

' Yes, it is usually in the drawing-room.'

' Of course. I remember.'

Mr. Don sets his teeth. ' Does that table suggest anything to you, Dick ? '

' To me ? Let me think. Yes, I used to play backgammon on it. What is it doing here ? '

' Your mother brought it in.'

' To play games on ? Mother ! '

' I don't—know that it was a game, Dick.'

' But to play anything ! I 'm precious glad she can do that. Was Laura playing with her ? '

' She was helping her.'

' Good for Laura.' He is looking at some slips of paper on the table. ' Are those pieces of paper used in the game ? There is writing on them : " The first letter is H—the second letter is A—the third letter is R." What does it mean ? '

' Does it convey no meaning to you, Dick ? '

' To me ? No ; why should it ? '

Mr. Don is enjoying no triumph. ' Let us go back to the fire, my boy.'

Dick follows him into the ingle-nook. ' But, why should it convey a meaning to me ? I was never much of a hand at indoor games.' Brightly, ' I bet you Ockley would be good at it.' After a joyous rumble, ' Ockley's nickname still sticks to him ! '

' I don't think I know it.'

' He was a frightful swell, you know. Keeper of the field, and played against Harrow the same year. I suppose it did go just a little to his head.'

They are back in their old seats, and Mr. Don leans forward in gleeful anticipation. Probably Dick is leaning forward in the same way, and this old father is merely copying him.

' What did you nickname him, Dick ? '

' It was his fags that did it ! '

' I should like to know it. I say, do tell me, Dick.'

' He is pretty touchy about it now, you know.'

' I won't tell any one. Come on, Dick.'

' His fags called him K.C.M.G.'

' Meaning, meaning, Dick ? '

' Meaning " Kindly Call Me God ! " '

Mr. Don flings back his head ; so we know what Dick is doing. They are a hilarious pair, perhaps too noisy, for suddenly Mr. Don looks at the door.

' I think I heard some one, Dick ! '

' Perhaps it 's mother ! '

' She may,' nervously, ' have heard the row.'

Dick's eyes must be twinkling. ' I say, father, you 'll catch it ! '

' I can't believe, Dick,' gazing wistfully into the chair, ' that she won't see you.'

It is a sadder voice than his own for the moment that answers, ' Only one may see me.'

' You will speak to her, Dick. Let her hear your voice.'

' Only one may hear me. I could make her the one ; but it would mean your losing me.'

' I can't give you up, Dick.'

Mrs. Don comes in, as beautiful as ever, but a little aggrieved.

' I called to you, Robert.'

' Yes, I thought—I was just going to——'

He has come from the ingle-nook to meet her. He looks from her to Dick, whom he sees so clearly, standing now by the fire. An awe falls upon Mr. Don. He says her name, meaning, ' See, Grace, who is with us.'

Her eyes follow his, but she sees nothing, not even two arms outstretched to her. ' What is it, Robert ? What is the matter ? '

She does not hear a voice say, ' Mother ! '

' I heard you laughing, Robert ; what on earth at ? '

The father cannot speak.

' Now you 're in a hole, father ! ' says a mischievous voice.

' Can I not be told, Robert ? '

' Something in the paper,' the voice whispers.

Mr. Don lifts the paper feebly, and his wife understands. ' Oh, a newspaper joke ! Please, I don't want to hear it.'

' Was it my laughing that brought you back, Grace ? '

' No, that would only have made me shut my door. If Dick thought you could laugh ! '

She goes to the little table. ' I came back for these slips of paper.' She lifts them and presses them to her breast. ' These precious slips of paper ! '

Dick was always a curious boy, and forgetting that she cannot hear him, he blurts out, ' How do you mean, mother ? Why are they precious ? '

Mr. Don forgets also and looks to her for an answer.

' What is it, Robert ? '

' Didn't you—hear anything, Grace ? '

' No. Perhaps Laura was calling ; I left her on the stair.'

' I wish,' Mr. Don is fighting for Dick now, ' I wish Laura would come back and say good-night to me.'

' I daresay she will.'

' And,' valiantly, ' if she could be—rather brighter, Grace.'

' Robert ! '

' I think Dick would like it.'

Her fine eyes reproach him mutely, but she says, ever forgiving, ' Is that how you

look at it, Robert? Very well, laugh your
fill—if you can. But if Dick were to appear
before me to-night——'

In his distress Mr. Don cries aloud to the
figure by the fire, ' Dick, if you can appear to
your mother, do it.'

There is a pause in which anything may
happen, but nothing happens. Yes, something has happened : Dick has stuck to his
father.

' Really, Robert ! ' Mrs. Don says, and,
without a word of reproach, she goes away.
Evidently Dick comes to his father, who has
sunk into a chair, and puts a loving hand
on him. Mr. Don clasps it without looking up.

' Father, that was top-hole of you ! Poor
mother, I should have liked to hug her; but
I can't.'

' You should have gone to her, Dick ; you
shouldn't have minded me.'

The wiser boy says, ' Mother 's a darling,
but she doesn't need me as much as you do.'

' I don't know.'

' That 's all right.   I 'm glad she 's so keen
about that game, though.'

He has returned to the ingle-nook when
Laura comes in, eager to make amends to
Dick's father if she hurt him when she went
out.

Softly, ' I have come to say good-night,
Mr. Don.'

' It 's nice of you, Laura,' taking both her
hands.

Dick speaks.   ' I want her to come nearer
to the fire; I   can't see her very well
there.'

For a moment Mr. Don is caught out again;
but Laura has heard nothing.   He becomes
quite cunning in Dick's interests.

' Your hands are cold, Laura ; go over to
the fire.   I want to look at you.'

She sits on the hearthstone by Dick's feet.

Shyly, ' Am I all right ? '

It is Dick who answers.   ' You 're awfully
pretty, Laura.   You are even prettier than
I thought.   I remember I used to think, she
can't be quite as pretty as I think her; and

L

then when you came you were just a little prettier.'

She has been warming her hands. ' Why don't you say anything ? ' she asks Mr. Don.

' I was thinking of you and Dick, Laura.'

' What a pretty soul she has, father,' says the boy; 'I can see right down into it now.'

' If Dick had lived, Laura, do you think that you and he—— ? '

With shining eyes, ' I think—if he had wanted it very much.'

' I expect he would, my dear.'

There is an odd candour about Dick's contribution, ' I think so, too, but I never was quite sure.' They are a very young pair.

Laura is trembling a little. ' Mr. Don——'

' Yes, Laura ? '

' I think there is something wicked about me. I sometimes feel—quite light-hearted— though Dick has gone.'

' Perhaps, nowadays, the fruit trees have

that sort of shame when they blossom, Laura ;
but they can't help doing it. I hope you are
yet to be a happy woman, a happy wife.'

'It seems so heartless to Dick.'

'Not a bit ; it 's what I should like,' Dick
says.

'It 's what he would like, Laura.'

'Do you remember, Laura,' Dick goes on,
'I kissed you once. It was under a lilac in
the Loudon Woods. I knew at the time that
you were angry, and I should have apologised.
I 'm sorry, Laura.'

His sweetheart has risen, tasting something
bitter-sweet. 'What is it, Laura ? ' Mr. Don
asks.

'Somehow—I don't know how—but, for a
moment I seemed to feel the smell of lilac.
Dick was once—nice to me under a lilac. Oh,
Mr. Don——' She goes to him like a child,
and he soothes and pets her.

'There, there ! That will be all right,
quite all right.' He takes her to the door.
'Good-night, my dear.'

'Good-night, Mr. Don.'

' Good-bye, Laura,' says the third voice.

Mr. Don is looking so glum that the moment
they are alone Dick has to cry warningly,
' Face ! ' He is probably looking glum himself, for he says candidly, ' Pretty awful
things, these partings. Father, don't feel
hurt though I dodge the good-bye business
when I leave you.'

' That 's so like you, Dick ! '

' I 'll have to go soon.'

' Oh, Dick ! Can't you——'

' There 's something I want not to miss,
you see.'

' I 'm glad of that.'

' I 'm not going yet ; but I mean that when
I do I 'll just slip away.'

' What I am afraid of is that you won't
come back.'

' I will—honest Injun—if you keep bright.'

' But, if I do that, Dick, you might think I
wasn't missing you so much.'

' We know better than that. You see, if
you 're bright, I 'll get a good mark for
it.'

' I 'll be bright.'

Dick pops him into the settle again.

' Remember your pipe.'

' Yes, Dick.'

' Do you still go to that swimming-bath, and do your dumb-bell exercises ? '

' No, I——'

' You must.'

' All right, Dick, I will.'

' And I want you to be smarter next time. Your hair 's awful.'

' I 'll get it cut, Dick.'

' Are you hard at work over your picture of those three Graces ? '

' No. I put that away. I 'm just doing little things nowadays. I can't——'

' Look here, sonny, you 've got to go on with it. You don't seem to know how interested I am in your future.'

' Very well, Dick ; I 'll bring it out again.'

Mr. Don hesitates.

' Dick, there is something I have wanted to ask you all the time.'

Some fear seems to come into the boy's voice. 'Don't ask it, father.'

'I shall go on worrying about it if I don't —but just as you like, Dick.'

'Go ahead, father; ask me.'

'It is this. Would you rather be—here— than there?'

After a pause the boy says, 'Not always.'

'What is the great difference, Dick?'

'Well, down here one knows he has risks to run.'

'And you miss that?'

'It must be rather jolly.'

'Did you know that was what I was to ask?'

'Yes. But, remember, I'm young at it.'

'And your gaiety, Dick; is it all real, or only put on to help me?'

'It's—it's half and half, father.'

'Face!' he cries, next moment. Then cajolingly, 'Father, K.C.M.G.!'

'When will you come again, Dick?'

'There's no saying. One can't always get through. They keep changing the password.'

His voice grows troubled. 'It's awfully diffi-
cult to get the password.'

'What was it to-night?'

'Love Bade Me Welcome.'

Mr. Don rises; he stares at his son.

'How did you get it, Dick?'

'I'm not sure.' Dick seems to go closer
to his father, as if for protection. 'There are
lots of things I don't understand yet.'

'There are things I don't understand either.
Dick, did you ever try to send messages—
from there—to us?'

'Me? No.'

'Or get messages from us?'

'No. How could we?'

'Is there anything in it?'

Mr. Don is not speaking to his son. He
goes to the little table and looks long at it.
Has it taken on a sinister aspect? Those
chairs, are they guarding a secret?

'Dick, this table—your mother—how could
they——'

He turns, to find that Dick has gone.

'Dick! My boy! Dick!'

The well-remembered voice leaves a message behind it.

' Be bright, father.'

Mr. Don sits down by the fire to think it all out.